The
Miracle
of
Music Therapy

The
Miracle
of
Music Therapy

EDITH HILLMAN BOXILL

Barcelona
PUBLISHERS

Photos on pages 96, 102, 106, 137, and 144
courtesy of Robert L. Beckhard

FIRST EDITION

ISBN 0-962080-8-5

2 4 6 8 9 7 5 3 1

Distributed throughout the world
by
Barcelona Publishers
4 Whitebrook Road
Gilsum, NH 03448
800-345-6665

Cover design by Frank McShane

PRINTED IN THE UNITED STATES OF AMERICA

With deep harmony, tender melody, and vibrant
rhythm this book is lovingly written for my family
Emily, Paul, Adrienne, Robert Jesse, Steve, Ben,
Jason, Lange, Maria Elena, Albertina with whom I
have sung many songs and I know we have been
listening to each other.

TABLE OF CONTENTS

THIRD MOVEMENT
CREATING A CONTEXT FOR PRACTICE

FOURTH MOVEMENT
THE MIRACLE IN ACTION

FIFTH MOVEMENT
THE TAO EXPANDS—GOING BEYOND
THE TREATMENT ROOM

SIXTH MOVEMENT
THE MIRACLE CONTINUES

INTRODUCTORY NOTE

"The Miracle of Music Therapy"! What a wonderful and engaging title for this book about Edith Hillman Boxill's journey. Her choice of title immediately tells us that music therapy has never been just an ordinary career for Edith but rather a way of life. In reading this engaging book you will come to see how her path in music therapy has always been inseparable from her life story.

I am fortunate to have traveled with Edith on this exciting journey of music therapy for almost twenty three years. I first met her in 1974 at an Urban Federation of Music Therapy Conference and heard her present her clinical work with autistic children. I felt an immediate resonance in what we thought and felt about music therapy—a resonance that has continued all these years.

Edith brings a deep understanding and empathy to each client that she works with in music therapy. In this book we have the privilege to meet some of these clients who have made re-markable changes. Their experiences show the power of music to reach the whole person—mind, body, and soul. These deeply human stories are touching and inspiring.

Throughout the book we come to know Edith's humanistic and transpersonal worldview.She believes that life can be a con-tinual process of growth and change, and that, per se, chronologi-cal age has no meaning. Edith views life as possibility, and is a model to those around her of being fully alive. She writes about taking music therapy beyond the treatment room and how music therapy can benefit all people.

Edith's work in recent years has been devoted to encour-aging music therapists to become more involved in finding solu-tions to important world issues, particularly the development of peaceful relationships among people. In the book she describes the birth and growth of Music Therapists for Peace and discusses some of its important projects such as Students Against Violence Everywhere—S.A.V.E.—Through Music Therapy. This program which Edith created and currently directs in the New York City Board of Education is one of her many contributions on the cut-ting edge of music therapy.

I have been told that in Chinese the word for friend is written with two characters. The translation is "to know or listen," "to the sound." Music Therapy is a way of life that asks us to listen carefully to the "sound or music" of others. Edith is someone who knows how to listen and is a true friend to so many clients and colleagues. It is a tremendous gift that Edith has given us this opportunity to read and listen to her Tao as a music therapist.

Barbara Hesser
Director of Music Therapy
New York University
September 1997

NOTES OF THANKS

My path as a music therapist has been directly influenced by Dr. Kenneth Bruscia, publisher of this book. The beginnings go back to my entrance into the music therapy program at New York University in February of 1973: it was with Ken that I took my first class; it was Ken who observed my first momentous breakthrough with autistic Kathy at Manhattan Developmental Center (MDC); and it was Ken who guided an independent study which evolved into my first published article, "Developing Communication with the Autistic Child through Music Therapy." In 1976 (when I was the director of the music therapy program at MDC and on the faculty of New York University) Folkways Records produced my LP Album, *Music Adapted, Composed, and Improvised for Music Therapy with the Developmentally Handicapped,* it was Ken who wrote a glowing review. And now his publication of *The Miracle of Music Therapy* is a new phase of our continuum. Only a song could do justice to this miracle!

Barbara Hesser has been a dear friend and key figure in my evolvement as a music therapist for over twenty years. She has given most generously of herself, being there for me in myriad professional and personal ways. Of exceptional importance, she brought about my appointment to the faculty of New York University. Just as her foreword and perceptive assistance during the writing of my first book, *Music Therapy for the Developmentally Disabled,* were invaluable, so throughout the writing of this manuscript have her discerning critiques added immeasurably to its clarity and quality. When Barbara queried, "Edi, did you mean such and such?" Or when she observed, "I got lost in this passage," I would listen, cogitate, and then dash back to my computer. Not least, her introductory note adds a beautiful and moving dimension to this book. I will be ever grateful that she is in my life.

Dr. Jerrold Ross, the first chair of the music therapy program at New York University, has a special place in my Tao as music therapist. When I applied for admission to the program in 1972, many years after getting the Bachelor of Music, I had my first interview with him. His support of my decision to train to be a music therapist at a mature age was heartening indeed. As he scanned my Curriculum Vitae, he assured me that having a broad spectrum of life experience was an asset. With a great sense of anticipation and joy, my journey as a music therapist had its formal start in February of 1973. And ever since welcoming me as a member of the faculty in 1975, Jerry has been a staunch advocate of my work in the field.

Although originally conceived fourteen years ago, it was Elaine Magidson and Jeff Sultanof who were catalysts for my reviving this book. At a birthday brunch for Jeff in December of 1995, while expressing his appreciation for my arranging this celebration he commented about my contribution to the field of music therapy. With earnest concern, he asked, "Edith, why aren't you writing another book—*your own story?*" Enthusiastically agreeing, Elaine who had been director of special education at Manhattan Developmental Center, added "Yes, that's a great idea. How about contacting Marcia Newfield–you know, the literary midwife. Maybe she could give you the jumpstart you need to get going." I agreed with Elaine and thanked Jeff for the much needed boost. In short order I started to gather the material from my files and went into action.

As suggested by Elaine, Marcia Newfield, a professor of literature did serve as a literary midwife. It was she who guided me in the first stages of reassembling the material that I had written those fourteen years ago. In our initial discussion, I stated that my intention was to create a book that could reach a broad audience, a book that would be serious yet still have a light touch. It would be for the lay public as well as professionals and its main goal would be to spread the word about music therapy. Her grasp of the subject matter, tone, and purpose were instantaneous. I arranged to have her view the manuscript as it emerged and have been tremendously fortunate to have her assist in its natural birth. It was Marcia who suggested the title *The Miracle of Music Therapy*.

John Keiser has significant connections to this book. Not only is he the son of Betty Keiser, the "angel" who paved the way for my becoming a music therapist, but he has also been my consultant in dealing with BJ Jasper (my computer, named after family members, *Ben, Jesse, Jason, Andy, Steve, Paul, Emily, Robert*). John has patiently flushed out and corrected technical flaws in the various drafts of the manuscript; and I have called upon him innumerable times to rescue me when my computer played tricks on me or when I played tricks on it. And through an amazing piece of software John was able to remotely control my computer and remedy the many glitches that mysteriously seemed to arise in my manuscript. Owing to him, I think the editor had a few less headaches!

Dr. Judy Weissman and I go as far back as 1973. She has contributed in creative and pragmatic ways to the work of Music Therapists for Peace, its Universal Peace Day events at the United Nations, and, most recently, another music therapy project called "Students Against Violence Everywhere—S.A.V.E.—through Music Therapy." Our mutual caring and sharing as colleagues and friends have an enlightening quality, a particular flavor that combines serious matters with a joyous sense that there are positive solutions to issues. Always making herself available in times of uncertainty and stress, and even during the single-minded intense days of writing this book, Judy's bright spirit, energy, and genuine faith in me invariably helped me in transcending these states.

While engrossed in the first revision of this book, I fortuitously benefited from Cella Roberts, a music therapist and music educator, who has a special gift for systematic planning. She had been following my progress during the various stages of writing this book, when I began to grapple with the proverbial writer's block. Taking Cella on a bird's eye tour of the contents, she scanned sections that were on the computer. She knew that my intention was to inform a broad spectrum of people about our field, to spread the word. The impact of viewing what I was working on for the first time filled her with excitement. This book now became an awe-inspiring reality that needed to be out there. So, what to do about that block! Her mind went to work immediately on how to organize the next stage that had been eluding me. Cella enabled me to finish the revision in record time.

Ron Granger, a music therapist, composer, and arranger, has used his musicianship and talents in computerized music to transcribe several of my original compositions included in this manuscript. Composed with Rafael Picorelli and arranged by Ron, "Save The World Through Music" is the theme song of the pilot school program conducted at The Lincoln Academy, a New York City junior high school: Students Against Violence Everywhere—S.A.V.E.—through Music Therapy. Ron has contributed an especially effective percussion arrangement of "No More Guns . . . Beat Drums!," a song that the students accompany with great gusto by adding their own improvised words and drumming.

xv

Ellen Gradenwitz's sensitive and knowledgeable assistance in the final stages of preparation of the manuscript eased the painstaking but rewarding task of dealing with queries, suggestions, and corrections of the proof reader. And, in the initial stages of the writing, Marian McGrath's book publishing know-how helped me make a number of important decisions with regard to technical matters.

At the Landmark Education Corporation, I have been pursuing a course of study entitled "Curriculum for Living." One of my projects resulted in the submission of the second draft of this book to my publisher *ahead of schedule*. This educational system is designed to open up unimagined possibilities for living the life that you love. A long-lasting "bonus" that came of the seminar called "Self-Expression and Leadership" is my relationship with Shabri Foy. Recognizing the value of music therapy and wanting to help inform the public, Shabri produced and hosted a cable television show on Music Therapists for Peace with a focus on a presentation of Students Against Violence Everywhere— S.A.V.E.—through Music Therapy. The show included videotapes of actual music therapy sessions with the students.

Without the many clients whom I have served and with whom I have shared my life over the years, this book would not have been possible. They have enriched my path as a music therapist and, in many instances, have shown me the way. To them, and others who follow, I extend the possibilities for attaining the full potential that music therapy offers.

And, dear reader, I invite you to look deeply into and between the lines of the book to feel and see and hear with me the profound sense of meaning and purpose that my loving family has given to my path as a music therapist.

PRELUDE

MY TAO
AS A
MUSIC THERAPIST

The only meaningful life is a life that strives for the individual realization, absolute and unconditional, of its own particular law. The undiscovered vein within us is a living part of the psyche; classical Chinese philosophy names that interior way "Tao," and likens it to a flow of water that moves irresistibly toward its goal.

—C. G. Jung, *Collected Works*

THE MIRACLE IS THE MESSAGE

> People usually consider walking on water or in
> thin air a miracle. But I think the real miracle is not
> to walk on water or in thin air, but to walk on
> earth. Every day we are engaged in a miracle . . . a
> blue sky, white clouds, the black curious eyes of a
> child—all is a miracle.
>
> —Thich Nhat Hanh

I invite you to accompany me on my Tao as a music therapist—a journey that will take you on my evolutionary path, from earliest recollections to the present. In his ancient book of wisdom *Tao Te Ching*, Lao Tzu tells us with simplicity and beauty that Tao means how things happen, how they work, that Tao is the single principle underlying all creation. That is all there is: Tao which is a principle and creation which is process.* It is with reverence that I have attempted to apply Lao Tzu's teachings to the writing of this book. A nonlinear process, it has evolved as a composition of words, music, and pictures about how things have happened and worked in the creation of my path as a music therapist.

Pondering about how and when I started my journey on this path, I wonder, Have I always been on it? Was it already in the stars? Or has the path been a series of lifelong choices? And, have even obvious milestones along the way been based on

---

* From *The Tao of Leadership: Lao Tzu's Tao Te Ching*, adapted by John Heider, Bantam Books, 1986.

choices that emerged from the deep inner source Jung speaks of? For, whenever anyone asks me how I came to be a music therapist, I fall into an introspective state, replying, "I can't put it in so many words. There's no one answer. Perhaps it goes back to early childhood memories of my mother's beautiful contralto voice, or further back to subconscious memories of her singing to me while in her womb, or even further back. On some level I know that I have been on this path for a long time. I may not always see it clearly, yet I know it in my heart."

This book is an awakening and exploration of my Tao, and at the same time, every word flows from it. The process of writing has been truly revelatory, bringing up feelings, perceptions, and memories that have heightened my awareness of who I am, where I have been, and where I am going—all aspects of Self. I have delved deeply into my evolution and reexperienced the joy and pain of being a musician, composer, music educator, and ultimately, music therapist.

To be sure, my path through music therapy has been tremendously gratifying, sometimes overwhelming, at other times disquieting, yet always worthwhile (to put it mildly). I have experienced highs and lows—feelings of exhilaration, growth, regression, despair, transcendence. But what has come through very strongly while writing this book is that my commitment to that path, and the inner knowing that I was on the "right" one, have guided me through frustrations and fulfillment, through disappointments and rewards, through uncertainties and successes. At the most unexpected moments I would be startled by belated revelations, exclaiming, "Did I *actually* do that? Was I aware of the courage—*coeur*—heart—it took? What an intuitive choice. It had great value and meaning but I haven't had a full appreciation of it until now! So *that* was the purpose for doing what I did?" There have been times of self-discovery, times of self-doubt, and times of great rejoicing in the choices I have made.

Tracing the steps of my path, and allowing long-forgotten memories to stream into conscious awareness has cultivated a deep knowingness, and affirmed my wholeness, my Gestalt, my Being. I feel enriched by new-sprung enlightenment and renewed by fresh views of "old" insights. For, while music therapy skills and techniques can be acquired and learned, the essence of being a music therapist is a *feeling choice* that emanates from a deep source within. And, music therapy is more than a career or a profession. It is a context that encompasses the totality of living for the therapist and the client—what I call *Music Therapy for Living* (Boxill, 1989). *Being a music therapist goes far beyond doing music therapy—it is a way of life.*

An underlying theme of my story is the oneness of my life and my work—the unfolding and interweaving of inner and outer realms of my evolution. Although words cannot do justice to the subtleties and nuances of any living process, the humanness and beauty and value that my chosen life's work holds for those who receive its benefits and those who offer its benefits will, I trust, shine through . . .

As my Tao as a music therapist has unfolded, I have also been awakened to the miracles of life, small and big, simple and complex, ordinary and extraordinary, humorous and serious. It is a thrill to sense, to be aware, to constantly remind myself that there are myriad happenings in our lives that are miracles. And, it is a thrill to send out the message that *the quintessential "theme and variations" of my Tao is the miracle of music therapy.*

THE TONE OF THIS BOOK

What is needed is nothing less than . . . a
methodology. . . concerning the highest
manifestation of life—the humanness of man.

— René Dubos

HOW THIS BOOK EMERGED

It was fourteen years ago that I started to write a book depicting
my evolution as a music therapist and some of my extraordinary
experiences with a variety of clients I worked with at Manhattan
Developmental Center (MDC) and the Manhattan Children's
Treatment Center. However, at the invitation of a publisher to
write a much needed textbook about this innovative treatment
modality for developmentally disabled people,* I set aside the
book that these years later has emerged as *The Miracle of Music
Therapy.*

    The "etiology" of the title is intriguing to me. Having been
asked any number of times by any number of colleagues and
friends why I haven't written a personal book—a book that would
be *my story*—I revived the originally conceived book. When I first
contacted a "literary midwife" and professor of literature, Marcia

---

* Originally published by AspenPublishers, Rockville, MD, 1985, the
book that resulted from this invitation is *Music Therapy for the Developmentally Disabled,* now published by Pro-Ed, Inc. Publishers.

Newfield, to discuss what I had already written, we were sitting on the divan in my living room, exploring the publishing possibilities for this book. She expressed a great interest in the subject— its broad appeal and its value for the average public as well as music therapists, other creative arts therapist, and allied professionals. She then asked me if I had a title for it. When I told her that I had been thinking of updating the original title, *My First Eight Years as a Music Therapist*, she suggested that there might be something more "catchy." Tuning in to her I said, "Oh, you mean something that would have popular appeal?" And she came up with, "How about *The Miracle of Music Therapy* as a possibility?" A light bulb flashed in my head. Enthusiastically I agreed, "Yes! Yes! *The Miracle of Music Therapy*."

Months later, while conferring with Marcia about my work-in-progress, I explained why I had changed the title to *The Miracle of Music Therapy: A Human Story*. I thought it would convey the quality I was seeking to transmit. Then, observing a fleeting moment of anxiety in my eyes when she suggested that I include more details of my life, Marcia queried, "What is it, Edith? Don't you know that we want more about what has gone into making you the human being—the music therapist—that you are today? Don't you know that *that* is the story we want you to tell us? When you talk and muse spontaneously, I hear your passion, I hear your music, I hear your miracle . . . I hear the miracle of music therapy in your unique story. Now write it—give birth to it!"

Writing a book is not just the time spent at the "drawing board." You eat it, drink it, sleep it, dream it. Salient and artfully hidden bits of material arise from the subconscious while walking along a certain street or gazing at a flowing river or fingering a blade of grass. Immediately, I scrawl these bits and pieces on any available paper, later to find their way into a particular passage that had been incomplete or needed an extra touch or lent itself to expansion into an entirely new segment. Often when that happens, my mind conjures up the image of George Bernard Shaw jotting ideas and thoughts wherever he happened to be—on scraps of paper while riding on a train, on napkins in restaurants, on theater programs. I couldn't be in better company!

When the book was submitted for publication, Dr. Kenneth Bruscia of Barcelona Publishers, sensitive to the personal quality of the book, suggested entitling it *The Miracle of Music*

Therapy: My Own Story and, in its final version simply, *The Miracle of Music Therapy.* So it is . . .

HOW THE BOOK IS DESIGNED

My intention has been to reach into the reader's heart and mind, raising awareness of the essences and benefits of a treatment modality little known to the public-at-large, or for that matter, to many health professionals. Because a book of this kind is meant for a diverse audience, I have deliberately avoided technical terminology, and have included theoretical explanations in the interest of communicating with clarity, enhancing understanding, and spreading the word.

Music therapy is a treatment modality that is applicable to and beneficial for people from the most severely disordered to the "normal." Since my concentration originally had been with developmentally disabled persons, the section devoted to anecdotal accounts deals in the main with persons who are so diagnosed. However, the essential perspective of the book as a whole is to stimulate possibilities for the expansion of the scope and influence of music therapy on individual, collective, and ultimately global bases. By *going beyond the treatment room*, the aim is to have music therapy available to anyone and everyone.

I like to think of this book as a symphony in six movements. A prelude, "My Tao as a Music Therapist," starts off with my view of what a miracle is, sets the tone of the book, and offers thoughts on the nature and unique qualities of music therapy. The first movement, "The Origins of My Tao," delves into beginnings and sources of my journey that signal the path I have chosen to follow. The second, "The Flow of My Tao," is a kaleidoscopic view of the direction my Tao took and the emergence of the call to be a music therapist. The third, "Creating a Context for Practice," explores the process of creating *A Continuum of Awareness*, a context that is intrinsic to my journey as a person and music therapist, and to the journeys of the persons I treat. With the assumption that we are all part of the same consciousness, a continuum of awareness is everyone's domain—a context for you, for me, for all people on varying levels. The fourth movement, "The Miracle in Action," invites the reader to take a "peek through a one-way mirror" at human beings undergoing remarkable changes—yes, transformations—that have come about through the processes of music therapy. The fifth, "The Tao Expands—Going Beyond the Treatment Room," rings out the benefits of music therapy for *all* people by presenting Music Therapists for Peace, Inc. (of which I am founder-director), and its main project Students Against Violence Everywhere—S.A.V.E. through Music Therapy. The sixth movement, "The Miracle Continues," addresses the essential humanness of music therapy and the future possibilities of this quintessential treatment modality to bring healing and health to our precious planet on all levels of existence—human and non-human. This intention is attainable for *we music therapists have as our therapeutic agent a universal means of human expression, MUSIC!* The Concluding Note is a loving tribute to my beautiful family.

THOUGHTS ON MUSIC THERAPY

> Parallel between New Physics and Music: Both are beyond language—we have to use language to *communicate* our inner experience which in its very nature transcends linguistics.
>
> —D. T. Suzuki

> Music therapy: The Universal Cure?
>
> —David Tame

A basic essence of the universe and esthetic means of expression, music has an extraordinary power to reach the human organism on all levels—the mind, the body, the soul; it has the power to heal, to expand conscious awareness, to stimulate the full spectrum of emotions and feelings. What, I ask, could be more natural than a therapy whose therapeutic agent is this universal form of human expression? Yes, music—one of humankind's most ancient and most natural means of expression, communication, and healing—has in comparatively recent years emerged as the therapeutic tool of the modern treatment modality, music therapy. And, although the processes of music therapy transcend verbal language, I am moved to share thoughts about this truly remarkable treatment modality and to express thankfulness for being on a Tao as a music therapist.

Music therapy is one of the most beautiful of therapies for both the client and the therapist: To receive and actively participate as a client in its benefits is a profoundly enriching and fulfilling life's experience; and to give service, as a therapist by nourishing a person's wellness through music is a profoundly enriching and fulfilling life's work. The essential purpose is the betterment of the client's way of living, the transfer of gains to a person's daily living process. It is what I call "music therapy for living," an opportunity to offer my clients a chance to live the miracle of music therapy as fully as possible.

As a participatory or experiential modality, music therapy involves people in their own healing, tapping into the healthy areas that exist in all of us. With wellness as the guiding force, the process is one of engaging the clients and the music therapist on a journey together, exploring and discovering the limitless benefits and influences that music can have. Deeply rooted in its historic heritage, this form of treatment is the conscious, skilled, purposeful use of music as a therapeutic tool for people of all ages, cultures, and diverse conditions. With a view to bringing harmony and balance individually, collectively, and ultimately globally, in nonverbal nonthreatening ways, it opens up new avenues for self-expression and behavioral change.

As a modern profession, this treatment modality had its beginnings in the United States when musicians volunteered their services to entertain wounded hospitalized veterans of World War II. Because the power of music had such positive effects on the physical as well as emotional well-being of these veterans, the need to establish a new therapy and develop a methodogy for its practice was recognized by the psychiatrist, Dr. Carl Menniger. In 1944, the first music therapy program to train qualified music therapists was instituted at Michigan State University. Today, there are over one hundred programs in colleges and universities worldwide: in North America, South America, England, Europe, Africa, the Middle East, and Asia. In this country, certification or registration to practice has been granted by the National Association for Music Therapy (NAMT) and the American Association for Music Therapy (AAMT). With the unification of these two associations as the American Music Therapy Association (AMTA), board certification will be granted.

Rehabilitative and preventive, music therapy is an art and a science that addresses the person holistically on psychological, physical, mental, social, and spiritual levels. Its benefits have been documented in a body of literature, including textbooks and professional journals, and Its efficacy has been proven in psychiatric and general hospitals, hospice programs, schools, community centers, developmental centers, substance-abuse rehabilitation centers, and correctional facilities, to cite a few.

Music is consciousness raising. It resonates on many organismic levels, contacts the sentient being with immediacy, evoking endless streams of sensations and feelings, from joyousness to excitement, sadness, hurt, love and more. Music serves as a therapy when it helps to establish a therapeutic relationship, nourishes growth, assists self-actualization, awakens a deeper understanding of Self, and heightens aliveness. Reaching in and bringing forth the expressive being is a two-way, reciprocal process of communication between the therapist and the person in treatment. This human contact through music therapy is fundamental to the relationship and to the music therapy process. Cultivating a caring and trusting client-therapist relationship, the music therapist accepts the here-and-now person with unconditional regard. Destructive behaviors are redirected or rechanneled. Techniques and skills that bring about successful experiences are applied. A basic tenet and attitude is that there are no *rights or wrongs*—that success and pleasure generate feelings of confidence and self-worth. Playing musical instruments, singing and chanting, and moving to music offer opportunities for functioning on higher and more gratifying levels while motivating learning and developing skills in many areas. They tap into the person's creativity, and bring fulfillment of "unsuspected" potentials.

Early on in my own search for an approach to the practice of music therapy that embodies the use of the attributes of music and the essences of humanness, I developed the context *A Continuum of Awareness* through music therapy. I was actually in training to be a music therapist when I began to explore experiences of "awareness" and "consciousness" and "aware consciousness" and "conscious awareness." And as I worked more in the field, these contexts and concepts of experience became fundamental to the creation of my approach to music therapy.

I found myself utterly fired by the perception that we are all a part of the same consciousness, that a continuum of awareness is everyone's domain, that it is the bridge we all use to move within realms of the unconscious, conscious, superconscious, and who knows what others. Thus, although my concentration has been the treatment of developmentally disabled persons, this context is for you, for me, for all people on varying levels. It has been intrinsic to my journey as a person and music therapist, and to the journeys of the people I treat. The continuum of awareness provides us with a context for awakening, heightening, and expanding awareness of all aspects of life and living; it is the path of consciousness to becoming and to being fully human.

Within this context the music therapist works to bring experiencing and relating to a person's conscious awareness on a continuum, thence to expression and purposeful action. This is a process of reaching in and bringing forth the expressive self that exists in varying degree in all of us, ultimately leading to the attainment of what Abraham Maslow calls "full humanness" (1976).

When I make personal gains along with my client; when the coexperiencing is empowering and enlightening for both; when music therapy becomes a gift for the client and for me, then I know its true nature and value. I am aware that we are resounding with the healing powers of music, that we are in tune and in synchrony with the rhythmic and melodic vibrations of the universe. In viewing the human being as a mind-body entity, music therapy falls within the purview of humanistic or third-force therapies and beyond to transpersonal or fourth-force therapies. The processes are dynamic explorations of the nature of human experience and the influence of music as it is applied therapeutically to people of all age ranges and who have a broad spectrum of conditions. This, I trust, you will experience vicariously in the movements of this book, and as you "peek through a one-way mirror" at what can take place through music therapy.

FIRST MOVEMENT

ORIGINS OF MY TAO

In our personal mythology our story ultimately is
told. . . . The sense of self is both immensely
powerful and at the same time . . . fragile. Our most
important task, though, is the gaining of self-
knowledge.

—Stephen Larsen, Ph.D.

SOURCES AND PATHWAYS

> . . . only human beings find their way by a light
> that illuminates more than a path of ground they
> stand on.
>
> — Peter and Jean Medawar

Eight decades ago, on November 8, I arrived on planet Earth. It is
my firm conviction that my journey, my Tao, has been to be a
music therapist. I know this in my heart, and each day I gain more
insights about it, insights that physician-philosopher Deepak
Chopra describes as inner visions that change our lives, a sudden
sense of knowingness that transforms us. He affirms: "When a
flash of insight first comes, it is not verbal, not linguistically
structured—it is a feeling of sudden knowledge, and is liberating,
because without words we know it as truth" (1994, p. 7).

   I feel that sense of knowingness about coming here and
being here as a music therapist. Once you can accept that you are
in exactly the right place at every moment of your life—not just
doing what you're meant to do but *being* who you're meant to
be—you can enjoy your own sacred journey.

   What was propelling me to be transformed? To enter a
new sphere? To reinvent myself? Was it a basic essence that I have
been searching to express? Do we create our own reality or does it
create us? Indeed, *there is an essential distinction between doing and
being.* I believe that the qualitative difference is unmistakable,
especially in the arts. You experience it when you get an instantaneous feeling-sense as to whether a musical composition or

painting or dance or poem, or any mode of creative expression comes genuinely from this *being* source.

CUES AND CLUES

While I'm writing this very section, I am having an insight that seems to explain the intrinsic presence of music in relation to my life, as well as everyone and everything in it. I don't *just* love music; making music is not *just* what I have chosen to spend my life doing; rather I have *the good fortune* to be a musician, *happily* I have a talent for music. And moving these insights even further along the continuum of my awareness, I realize that *being music* is who I am, is my core, my Self—that *being music* has made my Tao as a music therapist a natural one.

The sources of my Tao as a music therapist are both clear and complex at the same time. I am keenly aware that, in addition to being musical, being empathic and sensitive to others—their distress, their joy, their concerns, their kindliness, their needs, their wants—had beginnings in my early years. And as far back as I can remember, music has brought feelings of well-being and healing to my childish heart, and to my "grown-up" heart.

Revisiting my past experiences with music brings alive conscious memories, unconscious stirrings, forgotten events, and many provocative thoughts. It's not easy to face up to some, it's amusing to recall others; nevertheless, narrating the story of my musical life has been always enlightening. One of the insights that I have gained is that being musical and being empathic have been intertwined with an ongoing struggle to be my age. And so, before I can tell the story of my musical life, I need to explore what I now call the "too-young-too-old syndrome"—its origin and affect on the flow of my Tao.

TOO YOUNG OR TOO OLD

When I was five years old, I *cried* for piano lessons. I would not only stand at the side of the piano as if glued to it while my sister Gene was taking her weekly lesson, but I would plead with unrelenting persistence for my parents' consent to let me study too. Holding the misguided idea that a child had to be a certain age (what age I've never figured out), they thought it inadvisable to have me take formal music lessons as yet. But contrary to their view that I was *too young*, they finally succumbed to my passionate desire. And so, I started my "career" as a musician at the tender age of five.

After a few months of lessons, my highly perceptive mother remarked (as diplomatically as possible) to the piano teacher, "Mr. Ballad, I'm very pleased with the way Edith has taken to the piano, but I'm quite sure that she's not reading the music." "But that's impossible!" he declared indignantly. "Mrs. Hillman, you are very much mistaken. Just listen to her note-perfect playing." To which my mother challenged him with, "Well, let's find out. Why not test her? Have her play a piece that she hasn't heard before."

Yes, you've guessed it. I was playing everything by ear, which is not bad or wrong. On the contrary, it could be a positive sign—a sign of musical talent. However, even though my mother was aware of this, she expected that when one takes music lessons, one learns to read music. Indeed, she was there for me all the way as I continued to follow my natural path. But, read music I must!

Aware that it is not the content but rather *your perception* of the content that lends meaning to an idea or situation—for that matter, anything and everything—I have sought to shed light on the purpose that this paradoxical too-young-too-old syndrome has had for me. What did I need to discover about myself? Why the relentless tests of my authenticity?

Recently, in that search, I came across the following notes I had made that may be one clue:

> Tears of inexpressible meaning are pouring out of me
> as I write this. A secret which I have shared with a few
> chosen people (my close family and friends) may well
> be the obvious reason for being looked at and thinking
> of myself as too young until I reached twenty, and too
> old from then on. My earliest memory of an age
> "problem" was at four and a half. At that time,
> entrance to the first grade in the small Massachusetts
> town I lived in was five. Since I was born in November,
> I would have had to wait another year to enter school;
> but my loving, well-meaning mother didn't want me to
> lose a whole year of schooling. (Why? I often wonder.
> What was the hurry?) She bought the book that I
> would be using in the first grade and surreptitiously

taught me how to read so that I'd be prepared to enter school that September. My age became a deception that affected my contact with the other children who were the "right" age. In fact, I had to be secretive and prove myself worthy of being there.

Right age, wrong age. Wrong age, right age. Younger, older. Older, younger. Perception of myself was filtered continually through this "bugaboo."

At eleven, when I was halfway through the sixth grade, I was upgraded to the seventh. Being two years younger than the rest of the class put me at a disadvantage, especially with regard to one boy who had reached the sophisticated age of thirteen! But when I played Beethoven's tender piano piece "Für Elise" at a special class event, age was no longer a factor. I was relating, sharing, creating a connection with everyone in the room I felt at one with the very classmates I had been so removed from. And I could tell that they felt that way too. There was a silence when I finished that resounded like thunder in my ears. I knew I had reached them on a level that they had never before experienced. Was it the potential music therapist being tapped?

But, the specter of being too young or too old, never the *right* age, kept rearing its stubborn head. Entering high school at twelve caused me to be somewhat off center from the other students who were the *right* age. However, being a built-in "A" student, on the girl's basketball team, a contributor to the school journal, and increasingly involved in social activities, I gradually transcended "not belonging." A redeeming and rather odd feature of my high school in the small industrial town of Peabody, Massachusetts was that all programs, except the commercial course, were five-year programs, so that I would at least be sixteen when I graduated and would enter college at the "normal" age. In my senior year, I was filled with the excitement of the possibility of attending the Boston University College of Music and becoming a professional musician. I gave my all to practicing Bach fugues and Beethoven sonatas and Chopin preludes in preparation for admission. I entered Boston University that fall, close to the right age! I was seventeen.

Circumstances were such that I commuted by train from Peabody to Boston every day. Our home resounded with my father's carefully selected radio programs and recordings of classical music and opera. This was an enriching environment for me.

However, much to his disapproval, my musical taste was eclectic. He didn't quite relate to my, shall I say, free-flowing spirit. I would play popular music by ear with an abandon and freedom that was often abruptly short-circuited upon hearing his footsteps entering the living room where I would be blissfully ensconced at my beloved piano. My playing popular music, in his opinion, was not only wasteful but distasteful musically. This was a constant bone of contention between us. In fact, I can recall now with amusement how adamantly I argued in a futile attempt to convince him that popular music was, at the very least, appropriate for dancing. I even resorted to quoting the dean of the College of Music to counteract my father's opinion. Yet, and not surprisingly, he took great pride in this self-same daughter who, at the young age of thirteen, sang and played his favorite operatic arias from Verdi's *Rigoletto*. I guess there was a balancing force at work that nurtured my musical development.

I *lived* music throughout my college days, practicing, performing at concerts, sharing musical experiences with other students, rushing on Friday afternoons to attend concerts at Symphony Hall. Strangely enough, of the peak experiences I had over the four years, one I am amused to relate concerns a course in orchestral instruments: I finally realized a childhood desire to play the instrument that I had longed for (as had my father in his youth)—the violin. The professor, a well-seasoned violinist, was the only one who appreciated my efforts. For an entire semester I drove everyone else stark raving mad with the scraping tones that wafted through the air. I, however, was utterly entranced.

Yet more telling (and with modesty permitting) is the story of how my classmate and friend, Ruth Young, came to take piano lessons with my piano professor. Years after we had both graduated from Boston University, we were reminiscing about our musical experiences: her transferring to the College of Music after rebelling against her father's insistence that she major in business, our appearances together as a two-piano team, her twelve years as a music teacher in Santa Fé, New Mexico, and my years of facing many musical challenges. When I asked her how she happened to choose to study with my piano professor, Margaret Starr McLain, she assumed a sphinx-like posture and with a sly smile replied, "Edith, don't you know? *I just asked who the best pianist was. That led me right to your teacher and to you!*

Skipping along, it was after graduating from the Boston University College of Music, getting married, and living in New York City for eight years, that I did an about face. From being too young, I became too old! Twenty years later, when I met with Dr. Jerrold Ross, chair of the Music Department/Music Therapy Program at New York University to discuss the possibility of becoming a music therapist, I expressed my concern about starting a new career at an advanced age. He assured me that my life's experience was a great asset and that "mature" people were more than welcome, in fact, they were needed in the field.

I have been keenly aware of how my struggle with being the right age affected my existence. Often I avoided sharing things about myself with others, not only facts or information that would reveal my age, but also essential fibers of the very fabric of my life. I promised myself that I would resolve this conflict, When?

Well, at long last it happened. During a Landmark Education seminar entitled "Curriculum for Living," my inner voice commanded, with conviction and determination, "Enough of this! Enough . . . I have to be who I am!" Was this the phoenix rising? A rebirth? With heart pumping fast, face flushed, and voice wavering, I revealed my *exact* age—seventy-five—liberating myself from the too-young-too-old syndrome.

Since then this struggle—which had been an enigmatic necessity in my life— has become clearer bit by bit. I still wonder about it, how it shaped my evolution and what *its particular meaning is in my Tao.* Until the breakthrough, I had felt an interference, a kind of stoppage in the flow and spontaneity and passion that I knew were natural to me. Since reaching this turning point, I have been reactivating and re-creating my natural energy. Perhaps a saving grace and revealing aspect of my Tao was the fact that despite the "delays" and even long before the actual breakthrough, I've chosen to think of myself as *ageless.* I joyously, with great zest, have taken as my birthright the symbol of infinity, the horizontal figure of the number eight. And true to the mythical bird associated with the month of November, the phoenix* I have risen from my ashes over and over. I am feeling, physically as

---

* In Egyptian mythology, the phoenix is a bird said to live for 500 or 600 years and then consume itself by fire, rising from its ashes young and beautiful to live through another cycle, and is often used as a symbol of immortality.

well as emotionally, the lightening of spirit, the exhilaration of rebirth that comes of truly *breaking through*. What a sense of renewal, what a sense of balance, what a sense of aliveness when the shift in my perception occurred.

This certainly was confirmed by a pinnacle of my Tao that I reached in June of 1995. I was the recipient of the first ever American Association for Music Therapy Lifetime Achievement Award. Before the ceremony, the presenter had laughingly told me that there was thought of having a contest to guess my exact age. What, I wondered, had evoked or provoked such curiosity! Had my age become a cosmic joke? In any event, the idea was discarded because on second thought it might not please me. Well, surprise, surprise. I reversed a prepared acceptance statement from a rather serious, dignified speech, to jokingly telling about the contest that had been contemplated. I not only tossed it off, semi-humorously poking fun at myself, I announced, with newly-gained pride, my exact age. After a round of applause, a former student ran up to the podium and hugged me. With a new sense of admiration and inspiration, he exclaimed that he was aware of my approximate age—but *seventy-eight?*

My son Paul, daughter-in-law Adrienne, and grandson Ben, who knew and revered my venerable age, had come to celebrate this momentous occasion with me. The rest of my immediate family—daughter Emily and her husband Bob, granddaughter Jesse, and grandsons Steve and Jason—had sent word that they were there with me in spirit.

Despite the fact that I still have a tendency not to pinpoint dates of my chronology, I'm intrigued with speculating about what might have predated conscious memory and the lesson I needed to learn from having that specific "problem" show up. What effect did it have on my evolution as a music therapist? Perhaps one day I'll be able to approach the matter on the different levels and dimensions we humans are becoming aware of through the new physics. But for now, contemplating my evolution on a conscious level, I'll stay with the landmarks along the way that I perceive have shaped my identity.

I KNEW WHERE I WAS GOING

The psychologist, James Hillman, opens his book *The Soul's Code: In Search of Character and Calling* with these perceptive words:

"There is more to a human life than our theories of it allow. Sooner or later something seems to call us onto a particular path" (1996, p. 3). In June of 1939, after receiving the Bachelor of Music and working as an assistant to the dean at Boston University, I was on the verge of putting in a summer of graduate work at the University of Wisconsin. With figuratively one foot on the train to Madison, Wisconsin my plans changed abruptly. My friend Bill had for months been telling me about his cousin, Dr. Nathan Epstein, who, after getting his bachelor's from the Massachusetts Institute of Technology and his doctorate in biochemistry at Columbia University, had decided to become a medical doctor. A devotee of the arts and an amateur cellist, Nathan had combined studying medicine in France, Scotland, Switzerland, and Germany with extensive travel, collecting works of art, attending concerts, and absorbing the richness of European cultures. Now a pediatrician-heart specialist on staff at the Floating Hospital for Children in Boston, he was appointed to teach at the Cornell Medical School in New York City and conduct research in his specialty, rheumatic fever, at the New York Hospital starting the coming September. Bill thought that Nathan and I would have much in common and couldn't wait to introduce us. And, although art history and painting and dance were interests that we shared, it was my ardent rendition of Liszt's "Fifth Hungarian Rhapsody" that kindled the spark.

Did this music hold a promise for us? Had we been brought together to fulfill a purpose as yet to be revealed? Bill, too, had played the right tune. Nathan and I were on our wedding trip that very August!

Marriage brought me to New York City, the city of my musical dreams. I was ecstatic. I drank in the excitement of its energy. I would pinch myself to make sure that I was really walking along 57th Street, the cultural hub of the universe. Life was filled with music: study (piano and music courses for me, cello for Nathan), my music teaching, performing, our concert going, and socializing with musicians and artists. It was an idyllic time.

We saturated ourselves with Bach preludes and fugues, Mozart and Beethoven and Schubert piano sonatas and the haunting melodies from Glück's "Orpheus and Eurydice" that emanated from Nathan's cello. As a physician who was art-oriented rather than money-oriented Nathan's income was hardly lucrative. Fees for private practice were more often than not either

NEW YORK CITY BLUES

Words and Music
Edith Hillman Boxill

an original painting of an artist-parent or cello lessons with a musician-parent. And every dollar I earned from teaching went to music classes and lessons. Yet, we managed to get to concerts at Carnegie Hall such as I had fantasized during my student days in Massachusetts. We also managed for me to take classes at the Juilliard School of Music, the Dalcroze School of Music, a master piano class at the Mannes College of Music, and take private piano with Leonard Shure, a disciple of the renowned Beethoven interpreter Artur Schnabel!

And, in trying out my teaching wings in this great metropolis I was moving directly along an inevitable path. The potential to become a music therapist was working its mysterious ways: My brother-in-law Josh put me in touch with a musician/music teacher, Betty Krohn Keiser. The unfoldment of the loving friendship that developed had incredible meaning for my life's pilgrimage. Over the years, I came to call her "my angel." It was Betty who paved the way for me to teach at The Little Red School House, the Elisabeth Irwin High School, and the Metropolitan Music School. Some years after we first met, she was a key person in my relationship with Roger Boxill, *and was the crucial connecting link on my Tao as a music therapist.*

What a fulfilling period of my journey this was, not only musically but personally! Giving birth to my son Paul and my daughter Emily meant more to me than can be imagined or expressed (except through music). It's with a sense of awe that I retrace these two wondrous events in my life.

It was the fall of 1943. I had spent an ordinary day teaching at the Little Red School House. At 11 o'clock that evening an out-of-the-ordinary development in my path took place. I was at the Flower Fifth Avenue Hospital about to give birth to my first child. In the early morning hours of November 16, my son Paul was born with a caul enveloping his head. This is thought to be an auspicious omen and I agree with all my heart.

Then three years later, November 21, when I was teaching at the Mills College for Kindergarten Teachers, my sister Gene called in to say that I wouldn't be coming in to teach that day. Before she was able to tell the reason, the secretary asked with a note of concern, "She isn't ill, is she?" "Oh, no," my sister quickly assured her, "Edith's in seventh heaven. She gave birth to a beautiful baby girl this morning at the Flower Fifth Avenue Hospital!"

I love to think of my children as birthday gifts to me. We are three passionate music-loving Scorpios.

In addition to the joy that came of making music with my children, I was teaching, composing, and a professional accompanist/coach for a singer, Charles Riley. The latter led to giving a concert at Town Hall and a performance at Carnegie Hall. What a thrill to be on the stage of these hallowed concert halls that I had, in my student days in Massachusetts, dreamed of attending but hardly dared dream of performing in. We offered unusual programs that included Haitian music, my arrangements of Negro spirituals, and several of my original songs.

All along I was obsessed with, and perhaps possessed by, songwriting. Tunes or lyrics or both would buzz around in my head. Everything I did and saw was a possible song. It was at that time that I wrote a song in which I poured out my feelings about being in the city that might have been the place of my birth had my mother not made a sentimental journey from New York City, where she was living, to give birth to me in the city of her birth—Providence, Rhode Island (on Hope Street at that!). That song is "New York City Blues." Inspired by W. C. Handy's "St. Louis Blues," it not only has a niche in my heart because it reveals where I was emotionally at that time but it took on added significance: it proved to be the most exciting of my "near successes" in the popular song-writing world.

How Mr. Handy came to hear this special song is a happenstance that has enriched my life's journey. *Imagine having direct contact with a living musical legend—the venerable Father of Blues himself!* The singer mentioned above, having professional contact with Mr. Handy whose publishing company was in New York, arranged an appointment to perform the song in his office. Upon hearing it, Mr. Handy's response was immediate and enthusiastic—he wanted to publish it. To have *my Blues* published by *the* Father of the Blues was beyond my wildest dreams.

In the ensuing months I spent memorable moments with Mr. Handy—telephone conversations, visits in his office making preparations for the publication, listening to stories about his life. On one occasion he presented me with a copy of the historic W. C. Handy *A Treasury of the Blues* autographed in his inimitable handwriting. Not just an icon to be revered, he was a human being whose great warmth and spirit were uplifting.

HAITIAN SONG OF POSSESSION

Steady Beat

Frantz Casséus and Edith Hillman Boxill

Er - zu - lie! Er - zu - lie!

And so, filled with the prospect of his publishing my song, I left the city to spend the summer on Martha's Vineyard with my children and husband. I was to telephone from the Vineyard in September to arrange a meeting upon my return to New York. We would be finalizing the date of publication and the signing of a contract.

I have an everlasting memory of that phone call. It was now September of 1953. (Mr. Handy was in his nineties when I first met him in October of 1952.) Instead of Mr. Handy's voice which I had grown to know and had so looked forward to hearing, a strange voice informed me that he was no longer with us. My sorrow and disappointment were indescribable. I was inconsolable.

As I reflect on the meaning that Mr. Handy has had for me, on the meaning that the Blues have had for me, I wonder what effect this means of expression had on my evolvement musically and humanly. Could my affinity for this uniquely American form of musical expression, which I think of as a plea for humanness, have larger implications than I had any inkling of before? "New York City Blues" emerges constantly, reminding me of the transformation that I experienced from writing it, and the direct influence it had on therapy processes with clients. (See, for instance, "Donald's Blues," p. 122.) Could its importance possibly be another clue to the direction my life's work has taken, to Mr. Handy's place in my Tao?

A PERIOD OF TRANSITION

Music helped sustain me during a period of concern and uncertainty about my marriage. It was during that trying time that I got to know Geena Goodwin, a guitar teacher at the Metropolitan School of Music where I was giving music classes for young people. The many hours we spent playing music and sharing ideas about teaching developed into a friendship that I treasure to this day. It was at one of Geena's musicales in her studio-home that I met the art director of Columbia Records, Neil Fugita. Captivated by several of my songs, he was especially taken with "Lonely One" and submitted it as a possible recording by Johnny Mathis. Although that didn't happen, he engaged me to write music for an original film that he planned to produce. "Hora," written for one of the dance episodes, has survived and has found its way into my music therapy sessions.

And so, after twelve years of marriage, I went through the trauma and upheaval of divorce. For, although music had brought me together with my husband and was a strong bond between us, we parted ways. Yet, fresh musical adventures awaited me. Now a mother of young teenagers, I was teaching, performing, writing songs with a talented lyricist, Rhoda Roberts, and arranging concerts at the Metropolitan School of Music where I was on staff. While in the process of producing a concert for Black History Week, I learned of a Haitian guitarist, Frantz Casséus. An accomplished classical guitarist who had come to this country as the ambassador of music from Haiti but was unknown in this country, he was repairing guitars in a tiny out-of-the-way shop when I "found" him. After his successful "debut" at the Metropolitan Music School, he began to make concert appearances that I arranged for him. Frantz introduced me to Haitian music that became part of my repertoire and which I in turn introduced to a New York audience at the Town Hall concert mentioned earlier. Also, we collaborated on the composition of a "Haitian Piano Suite,"* my recording of which was presented to the president of Haiti. Interest in Haitian music led me to submit a proposal for a Ford Foundation grant to study the indigenous music of Haiti and its African origins. In preparation for this study, I took a trip to Haiti with my daughter and son, recorded music, bought drums, and got a wonderful taste of the country and its people. The music of Haiti has been dominant in my work, first as a musician and to this day as a music therapist.

---

* "Haitian Song of Possession" from this suite is included in my cassette *Music Theraphy with the Developmentally Handicapped*, The Smithsonian Institution Folkways Cassette Sereies 06180.

EMERGENCE OF THE CALL

> Imagine fate as a momentary "intervening
> variable." Rather than as a constant companion . . .
> fate intervenes at odd and unexpected junctions,
> gives a sly wink or a big shove. . . . Fate does not
> relieve me of responsibility; in fact, it calls for
> more.
>
> — James Hillman

The call to be a music therapist had been gaining momentum and
energy and strength throughout the many vicissitudes of my
journey. Was it inevitable that it be heard? Would I have the freedom to answer? According to Rollo May (1978), the personal freedom to think and feel authentically is the foundation of values
such as love and courage. He contends that freedom is how we
relate to our destiny, and destiny is significant only because we
have freedom.

A TURNING POINT

Again my "angel " Betty Keiser was waving her magic wand! Af-
fectionately combining personal with professional assistance, she
played a unique role in my Tao as music therapist. Through her, I
was moving toward a milestone; indeed, was on the brink of a
turning point. The freedom that May talks about was coming into
view as was the sly wink or shove that Hillman (1996) refers to.
It was Betty's sister Jane Harris, a music therapist, who would
introduce me to music therapy.

During the ten-year period of being a single mother of two children, I had become a familiar figure in the Harris household as friend and "holiday celebrations pianist." A houseguest at Jane's summer home in Westport, Connecticut in August of 1964, I was to meet another houseguest, Roger Boxill, an actor/director and a candidate for the doctorate in dramatic literature at Columbia University. There we were in this spacious house doing our separate "things," I in the living room practicing one of my favorite Schubert sonatas, the A Major, he upstairs helping rearrange rooms for weekend guests. Although we hadn't as yet come in contact, I was aware of his presence, of a subliminal connection. Somehow, not only did the Schubert seem, in a mysterious way (or was it my imagination working overtime?) to be creating this link, but earlier in the morning, before meeting him face to face, I heard his resonant, well-modulated speaking voice. Its effect on me was instantaneous. It foretold the golden tenor that was to bring us unforgettable musical moments and was a catalyst for the charismatic relationship that led to my second marriage. Rodge's voice and my piano blended in arias from Bach's *St. Matthew's Passion* to Handel's *Messiah* to Bernstein's *West Side Story*.

Jane's home in New York City had become the setting for an informal musical ensemble. We enjoyed music making that became a built-in part of holiday celebrations. Filling the air with Christmas carols, Thanksgiving songs, and choral and instrumental compositions of Vivaldi and Handel and Schubert, our ensemble consisted of Betty on the recorder, Jane on the violin, I on the piano, and Rodge singing. Together, we would all joyously ring out holiday songs, especially favorite Christmas carols.

It was the Thanksgiving dinner in 1971 that marks a crucial passage in my Tao as music therapist. After incredibly inspired music making, Jane came out with this startling statement: "Edith, I think you're a natural for the music therapy profession! Everything points to it—your musical ability, your life experience, your personal qualities. By the way, there's a presentation on music therapy next Wednesday evening. Can you make it?"

Could I make it? A deep, deep chord resounded in the depths of my being. I heard the call to be a music therapist !

MOVING TOWARD THE CHOICE

Once the call emerged, the choice was yet to be made. What about the self-exploration and the self-doubt; and the mindfulness that dealing with other people's "problems in living" carries a powerful responsibility? It was reassuring that having had individual and group therapy over a number of years—in my view, essential components of preparation for being a therapist—provided me with a strong foundation.

Whirling about in my mind were all manner of insights and thoughts about the order in which my path was unfolding and enfolding. David Bohm, the distinguished physicist, tells us of the generative order: "This order is primarily concerned not with the outward side of development . . . but with a deeper and more inward order of which the manifest forms of things can emerge creatively. . . .*This will lead to the implicate order* (my italics) . . . found to have a broader significance . . . in . . . [the] consciousness [of each human being]" (1987, p.151). Very often, on a level of conscious awareness that goes beyond the realm of understanding, I stop and ponder the mystery of what the human being is, who we are, what we are, why we are. I wonder about the possible rhyme or reason of the order of things. However, we humans are on the quest, aren't we?

Furthermore, in viewing my journey, on obvious levels it seems that by majoring in piano and minoring in psychology at Boston University, I anticipated the direction I would take to become a music therapist. It comes clear that throughout my college years there was a growing awareness that musical expression goes far beyond performance, that there must be a greater purpose than being able to play or re-create music on a note-perfect level for performance. On the one hand, I began to reevaluate going through a period of envying Manuel, also a piano major, whose technical facility was equal to that of the formidable Glenn Gould (but hardly equal to his musicality). On the other hand, the quality of my playing was, from all reports and from my own sensibilities, in a completely different sphere. Was this growing awareness another precursor of the path I would be taking?

My innate proclivity was to create music for reaching the listener on the many human levels, not to perform, per se. I marvel at how elemental and instinctual it has been, as a musician and now as a music therapist, to "know" this, to embody the precept of the great humanitarian-musician, Pablo Casals: "Music must serve a purpose; it must be a part of something larger than itself, a part of humanity . . ." (1970, p. 51); and, to live by his peace-loving declaration at the United Nations in October of 1963: "Music, that wonderful universal language, should be a source of communication . . . I once again exhort my fellow musicians throughout the world to put the purity of their art at the service of mankind in order to unite all people . . . " (1970, pp. 288 & 289).

Although the subterranean level of knowing my true calling was always there, it was when interviewed years later by a newspaper reporter about my work as director of Music Therapy at Manhattan Developmental Center and the hows, whys, and whens of becoming a music therapist, that in a flash, with a shift of perception, my whole being was flooded with the conscious awareness of the realization that I had actually been preparing to be a music therapist *all my life*!

And, looking back, I found myself recalling an experience which had been merely a fond memory but now took on a significant connection between my past and present, an incident that occurred *before* the modern profession of music therapy had been established. At Boston University, instead of a written thesis, piano and orchestral instrument majors "played" our theses. A Bachelor of Music degree requirement was a two-hour concert in the University Concert Hall. Four years of intense work went into this culminating event which was essentially our debut as professional musicians.

An hour before my closest friend and classmate, Ruth Young, was to give her graduation concert, we were together in a student's lounge that had a practice piano. To her surprise (ordinarily she took matters in stride with a kind of bravado), she was quite agitated, not just with the jitters, not just with butterflies in her stomach. She was having a full-blown attack of stage fright. Instinctively, intuitively, instantaneously, I knew what above all else could help her through this crisis, what could help her reach a state of equilibrium. Gently and silently, I led her to a couch and motioned that she lie down. Being well aware of sharing a love of Chopin nocturnes, I asked her in muted tones, "Would you like to have me play a Chopin nocturne for you?" She managed an almost inaudible, "Yes, Edith. Yes . . . "

For the better part of that hour, the Nocturne in D wafted through the air, creating a peaceful, harmonious atmosphere in which Ruth readied herself "to face her music"! Now, in retrospect, I have the distinct feeling-sense that this was a *precognition* of my Tao as music therapist.

I MAKE THE CONSCIOUS CHOICE

One day, while getting closer and closer to making the choice to follow the path that deep down I knew was my truth, I was at the home of the very same Ruth, now a music educator in New York City. Over the many years, we shared much history together, shared our innermost thoughts and dreams with each other. As we both pondered the possibility of a momentous turning point in my life, she handed me a well-worn book, saying to me with a look of wisdom-of-the-ages, "I think this will speak to you." I saw the title, *Teacher*.*

My curiosity was very much aroused. How would this book relate to my becoming a music therapist? I was facing the choice of going back to school to become a music therapist many years after taking my bachelor's degree. Clearly, at this juncture my path was taking a new course. Being extremely perceptive, my dear friend had a sixth sense about the push I needed to take the quantum leap into this uncharted path.

I had read every available book on music therapy I could lay my hands on. I devoured them as if satisfying a deep hunger in me. But what special message did this book of Sylvia Ashton-Warner, a teacher of New Zealand aboriginal Maori children, hold for me? Her words speak for themselves:

> . . . I've always allowed for miracles in everyday life. I *expect* them! (1964, p. 125).

> I see the mind of a five-year-old as a volcano with two vents; destructiveness and creativeness. And I see that to the extent we widen the creative channel, we atrophy the destructive one (1964, p. 29).

Indeed, I was transfixed by her integrity, her spirit, and her unorthodox (in the view of the education authorities) approach to teaching. Because the children would be singing or

---

* Syliva Ashton-Warner's *Teacher*, Banam Books, 1964. The magnificent, personal story of an amazing woman and her inspiring new method of teaching based on joy and love.

dancing or digging into a barrel of clay instead of sitting quietly in their seats, (as any good teacher knows that all children should!) her classroom, called "infant room," was viewed to be disorderly.

The way this extraordinary teacher handled a critical matter is the core of her deeply felt humanity. The Maori children resisted learning to read *Janet and John* books and other scientific English books, so aptly categorized by Ashton-Warner. Such books bore no relation to these children's lives. Yet, it was necessary to satisfy the school authorities who had scheduled an annual evaluation of the state of the infant room. An original, creative teacher, she reached her "little ones," as she lovingly called them, where they were: their feelings, their interests, their daily lives, their families. *Her imaginative solution to having the children learn how to read was to have them create their own books in what she called their "organic or key vocabulary"*—their organic language, which she described as a growing, living, changing design, normal and healthful, unsentimental and merciless and shockingly beautiful. In essence, they wrote about what was natural for them, what was happening in their lives. Following is a sampling from Ashton-Warner's inspirational book (pp.152–153):

> Mummy is crying
> because Daddy
> hit her in the face.
>
> Daddy got wild
> and I got
> wild because
> Daddy was drunk.
>
> When I got
> up I got
> ready for school
> and I hurried
> because Daddy
> was wild
> and he looked cross.
>
> I got a growling
> last night
> because my
> sandals were
> wet.

> I fell out of
> bed so Daddy told
> Mummy to
> shift over.

It was through this caring acceptance of and regard for their "organic language" that the Maori children learned to read. By the time the school officials made their visit to this *not-run-of-the-mill* classroom, the children were willing (however, reluctantly) to read the traditional books. Their teacher got a passing grade!

That very night I read *Teacher* from cover to cover. The message was loud and clear: If there is "organic language," there must be "organic music." Aha! I thought. So this is what music therapy is about. So this is what it would mean to be a music therapist: In the broadest and simplest terms, it was to assist in the development of a person's healthy Self through uncovering, bringing to light, the music that is an integral part of being human. In my readings on quantum physics, I came upon this wonderful corroboration that we are not matter, we are music.

I made the conscious choice to become a music therapist.

SECOND MOVEMENT

THE FLOW
OF MY
TAO

Tao cannot be defined . . . . Even though Tao is the source of all growth and development . . . Tao benefits all without prejudice . . . . The work is done in order to shed the light of awareness on whatever is happening: also, selfless service, without prejudice, available to all.

—Lao Tzu, *Tao Te Ching*

(adapted by John Heider)

MY TAO TAKES DIRECTION

> Music is a bridge between the abstract and the
> tangible, between imagination and reality . . .
>
> —Yehudi Menuhin

Now a tangible reality, the training to become a certified music therapist took place well over thirty years after I had earned my Bachelor of Music degree at Boston University. Entering the music therapy program at New York University in February of 1973, I came out holding the Master of Music Therapy in June of 1974.

A vivid memory of what state I was in makes me smile and weep at the same time. My first interview when applying for admission to the New York University Music Therapy Program was with Dr. Jerrold Ross, then chair of the Department of Music/Music Therapy. With a catch in my voice, I expressed my regret at not coming to this profession sooner. But upon handing him my curriculum vitae, with my diversified background in music, painting, dance, and life experience, I was heartened by his assuring words: "You're the mature kind of person that we need in this field." And then, with an engaging sense of humor and twinkle in his eyes he added, "Remember me when you're rich and famous!"

A music therapist famous? Possible, but improbable. Rich? That thought sent my mind off on a tangent: If I had entertained the notion of being rich, I certainly would have pursued a very different path. As a matter of record, throughout my journey into adulthood, the incentive to make money has never been a priority or an ideal. Quite the opposite. The following experience as a neophyte music teacher was a rude awakening and made a lasting impression.

The story goes this way: I had the dubious honor of giving piano lessons to the child of an extremely wealthy family in my hometown of Peabody, Massachusetts. The fee for the piano lessons was *one dollar* an hour. One day I arrived at this family's mansion fifteen minutes late, breaking my habitual promptness for, I'm certain, a valid reason which I don't have a clear recollection of. I would willingly have made up the time. But no such thing. Payment for the lost quarter of an hour was deducted! Had I not been concerned about the innocent child involved, I wouldn't have stepped inside that mansion ever again.

Other memories that dealt with fame and fortune raced through my mind: I had almost "made it" when I dipped my hands into the New York City songwriting waters. I loved writing songs that came directly out of my experience—songs like "New York City Blues" which the Father of the Blues, W. C. Handy had planned to publish, "Lonely One" which Columbia Records held for four months, and "The Smile You Wear" which was recorded as a single and included on an LP album. But the commercial crassness that spelled success in that world went completely against my nature. (One bonus did come of these "near successes"—membership in and registration of over twenty of my songs with ASCAP, the American Society of Composers, Authors and Publishers.) Exposure to the harsh competitive world may have been one of life's lessons I needed to learn but under no circumstances did I want to be part of it. Whenever this is the subject of conversation, I say, *with feeling,* "Good that I didn't make it in that world. *'Cause if I had, I might not be a music therapist today."*

Now, to the matter at hand. When I entered the music therapy program, one professor cautioned, "If you were eighteen and on wheels *perhaps* you could handle the course load you've undertaken." Well, I wasn't eighteen and I wasn't on wheels. But I was determined to go through the master's degree program in a year and a half. I knew that was what I was meant to do. The training promised to be an adventure into new and enriching domains. My mind set—my heart set—was that the marathon run would be nonstop from February of 1973 to June of 1974.

And so it was back to school. What a turning point this was! I was actually embarking on my Tao as a music therapist.

Aware that there is a vast difference between being perfunctory and being passionate about what you're intended to be, becoming a music therapist implied that I had the possibility of actualizing my full potential.

Because the music therapy program at New York University was in the process of formulation, I was in the fortunate position to be able to design a course of study that would cover all the requirements and include subjects that dealt directly with the specialized work I was already involved in at Manhattan Developmental Center. Basic courses were in theories and principles of music therapy, abnormal psychology, and childhood psychology. Electives that I chose covered a variety of subjects in different departments such as Music of the Nonwestern World, Activities for the Developmentally Handicapped, and Music in Child Education. I wrote papers entitled "The African Heritage of Haitian Music," "The Libido According to the Gospel of Freud and Jung," "Imaginary Conversations with Carl Rogers, Fritz Perls, and Iztak Bentov," and "The Child's First Experience of Self-Awareness." I took one pass/fail course just to see if I could break the pattern of my longtime built-in pressure to get As. I worked just as hard!

One day after hours of delving into a book on childhood and adolescent psychology, I needed a change of pace. After Schubert's Sonata in B Major had worked its musical magic, I thought I might have a bit of mindless diversion by watching television before getting back to the books. Who knows what might turn up on a Saturday afternoon? I settled in for some entertainment. I wasn't quite prepared for what happened!

On the screen was a figure that I instantly recognized without ever having seen him before! It was B. F. Skinner whose behaviorist theories and practice were completely antithetical to the humanistic psychology I embraced and was deep into studying. This, I told myself, was hardly the entertainment I had anticipated treating myself to. As I flicked—today it would be surfed—to other channels I stopped suddenly. My attention was drawn to a person dressed in loose white garments sitting in the lotus position and surrounded by a beautiful array of flowers. My ears perked up to hear a gentle singsong voice speaking about Transcendental Meditation (TM)™. I soon realized that I was witnessing the voice and presence of the Maharishi Mahesh Yogi, founder of TM. Fantastic! I listened intently to the benefits that came of meditating regularly for twenty minutes in the morning and late afternoon—an adjustment of Eastern practice of meditation to fit the lifestyle of the Westerner. These benefits included the heightening of awareness, enhancement of creativity, release of stress, and much more. I later learned that Dr. Herbert Benson of Harvard University Medical School found TM advantageous for his patients and that Deepak Chopra of quantum healing fame combined his Western medical training with the teachings of the Maharishi.

This turned out to be the kind of synchronicity that was a constant source of enrichment for me. Having previously heard about Transcendental Meditation, I had seriously considered looking into where and how I could learn about it. And here was the founder of this very form of meditation speaking directly to me—telling me exactly what I wanted to know—and appealing precisely to the very states of being that I was totally immersed in developing for myself and for others. I made careful note of the address of the Center where it was taught and was there the very next Monday evening. TM became an invaluable tool. Many a late afternoon I found as quiet a spot as possible in Washington Square Park (no easy accomplishment!) and cleared my mind-body of exam-taking tension or helped renew my energy level. I can say unequivocally that the walk to receive my degree was facilitated by the meditation that I engaged in regularly twice a day.

PROFESSIONAL ENTRANCE INTO THE FIELD

Being a "mature" candidate for the degree proved to be in my favor. My life experience and broad knowledge of the field of music were preparation for what lay ahead. Before I actually entered the program, my desire to be actively involved in the field of music therapy had led me to do volunteer work at the Manhattan Children's Treatment Center on Ward's Island. Once in the program at N.Y.U., the volunteer work I did at Manhattan Developmental Center (MDC) evolved into the requisite internship. Upon becoming a certified music therapist, I had so thoroughly demonstrated that music therapy was indispensable for this client population that I was given the go-ahead to create a music therapy program. At an institution where music therapy had not only been unknown but was highly questionable in the eyes of a behavioral psychologist (who reigned supreme), this was indeed a coup.

In the face of a two-year ongoing dialogue on the behaviorist versus humanist approach to treatment and to life, I forged ahead fully committed to my orientation, developing a music therapy program that was making a decided impact on the welfare of the clients. One day, the above-mentioned psychologist attended an in-service training for newly-employed aides in ways of assisting in music therapy sessions. Smiling broadly, out of the blue he said he had something to say. In light of our opposing points of view, I could hardly believe what I heard. He declared (in true-confession style), "When Edith arrived at MDC, I must say that I didn't know a thing about music therapy. I figured that we already had recreation therapy. What was the difference? Well, I must tell you that after seeing the amazing results that Edith has had with our clients—the improvement in their functioning physically, cognitively, emotionally, interpersonally, and the actual changes that have taken place—I've done an 180% turnabout. Now I certainly can see how different music therapy is from recreation therapy. Now I know why she's here . . . "

HOW I FOUND MANHATTAN DEVELOPMENTAL CENTER

It is interesting to note that it was twenty-three years ago, at the time that Manhattan Developmental Center (MDC) was a replacement for the notorious Willowbrook State School for developmentally disabled persons on Staten Island, that my work as a certified music therapist began. After Geraldo Rivera's earthshaking exposé of the scandalous nightmarish conditions at that residence, MDC, a new and improved State facility for developmentally disabled persons, was to be the home for the casualties of Willowbrook. In 1975, after the transfer of all its residents, the doors of Willowbrook were closed. As I write this in 1997, a recently made film with Geraldo Rivera as commentator—"The Unforgotten: Twenty-five Years After Willowbrook"—has been showing at a theater in New York City. It is a plea for treating people humanely.

Finding MDC was directly connected with the volunteer work I had been doing at the Manhattan Children's Treatment Center on Ward's Island. I had become involved in the welfare of one particular young boy of eleven named Darryl. When he was about to be transferred to another facility, I made every effort to learn where he would be placed, but to no avail. In my search for him I found MDC. Darryl was not there, but my unheralded appearance led to volunteering my services for its treatment program. The head of recreation therapy, Ellen Ashton, immediately welcomed me as a much needed addition to this institutional setting.

Nothing is accidental! Out of this fortuitous circumstance the requisite music therapy internship resulted. I would spend the academic year and the next thirteen years at MDC bringing the benefits of a beautiful treatment modality—music therapy—to people who had little or no beauty in their lives.

Starting in the fall of 1973, I experienced many rewarding hours, many agonizing hours, many gratifying hours, many heartrending hours, many joyous hours. The effect of my work on the clients so impressed the administrators that I was engaged—employed!—to be on staff as a music therapist once I graduated from N.Y.U. Moving into this stage of my Tao in June of 1974 as a certified music therapist was an exciting "plunge" into the field of music therapy.

SPREADING THE WORD

> One begins to know things by a different kindof
> experience, more direct, not depending on the
> external mind and the senses . . . . There is a new,
> vast and deep way of experiencing, seeing,
> knowing, contacting things . . .
>
> — Sri Aurobindo

When I stepped across the threshold of a large granite building bearing the name Manhattan Developmental Center, I entered into a new and unfamiliar world. Never before had I been exposed to a broad range of developmentally disabled persons who functioned from close to "normalcy" to those whose multiple handicaps rendered them physically and mentally incapacitated. Yet intuitively I knew what I needed to do—what I needed to be. Effortlessly, I was very soon deeply involved in their lives. Through the approach to music therapy that I created—*A Continuum of Awareness*—they began to experience music in ways they had never experienced it before, in ways that aroused and raised their awareness, and that stimulated a
newfound aliveness. I experimented, explored, applied specific methods to reach them, to involve them in actively participating in singing, using simple musical instruments, and moving to music. I learned from them. I learned to love them.

    Word of this virtually unknown treatment modality spread. My work burgeoned in New York State as well as nationwide. Expanding the scope of the field by introducing music therapy to the national organization that is an advocate of developmentally disabled persons—the American Association on Mental Deficiency (AAMD)—was an innocently "heroic" act. At a conference in New Orleans, an occupational therapist declared that I had opened up "the world of music therapy " to her and to the organization. For until then the prevalent misconception about music therapy, if known or thought of at all, was that it was just another kind of recreation therapy: sing-alongs and playing musical games and having fun with music. As with the psychologist at MDC, wasn't that what it was all about? Occupational therapy, physical therapy, speech therapy, recreation therapy were integral parts of the programming for people with developmental disabilities. But why music therapy? What could it do for the developmentally disabled, especially the mentally retarded, that recreation therapy was not already doing?

What an educational job I had taken on! AAMD was about to find out that music therapy had a great deal to do with developmentally disabled people. It was also about to learn that the practice of music therapy by a qualified music therapist requires multidisciplinary training in music therapy methodology, musicianship, psychology, and the behavioral sciences, as well as knowledge of the many schools of psychotherapy; that clinical experience as a music therapy field worker and intern are requisites of the training and preparation to enter the field as a practitioner; that empirical studies and research give evidence of its efficacy; that in addition to implementing its own treatment goals, music therapy has proved to be a primary treatment modality for this client population, an aid to diagnosis, and a reinforcement for occupational, physical, and speech therapies. AAMD was also about to be informed that there are other creative arts therapies— art, dance, and drama—that enhance the growth and development of our clients and give enjoyment to their lives.

And find out it did. During ensuing years, as a professor of music therapy at New York University and the director of music therapy at MDC, I was totally committed and dedicated to presenting and demonstrating the nature of music therapy and the other creative arts therapies as distinct disciplines at national conferences held throughout the United States. An upstream struggle, I solicited and got support from well-established music therapists as well as other creative arts therapists. Through the efforts of a few key members of AAMD who became convinced of the value of music therapy in particular, I was invited to participate in a board meeting of the national committee. After a concise delineation of the nature of music therapy as a treatment modality and the training required to become an accredited music therapist, the president, *appearing* to be receptive and understanding, thought he was acknowledging me by saying, "We see that music therapy—*as the child of recreation therapy*—could be included in the recreation therapy division of AAMD." I heard myself saying, "Oh no!" as my barometer of frustration rose precipitously. However, I managed to say calmly, "Music therapy is an autonomous discipline for which rigorous training is required. I speak as a faculty member of New York University and a music therapist certified by the American Association for Music Therapy."

Victory! There was consensus that I submit a petition to the board for the purpose of establishing a separate creative arts therapies subdivision. I spent long hours collecting the requisite number of signatures. Subsequently, the board voted it in and I became its program director, arranging yearly presentations, workshops, and seminars by leading music therapists, art therapists, dance therapists, and drama therapists in such cities as Washington, San Francisco, Denver, Miami, and Detroit.

One significant outcome was in relation to the textbook I would be writing. Returning from a presentation at the AAMD national conference in Detroit, I waded through a stack of mail that had accumulated during my absence from MDC. I finally got to a large manila envelope at the bottom of the pile. One of those wearisome advertisements, I thought, but I'd better see what it is before discarding it. Well! My mind went into a spin. It was hardly an advertisement. It was a packet with a cover letter from Mr. R. Curtis Whitesel, educational director of rehabilitation and special education of Aspen Publishers, Inc. inviting me to write a handbook on music therapy for the mentally retarded. Since this invitation had been sitting on my desk for a week, I took the request to answer immediately very seriously. After ten minutes of intense thought and decision making, I breathed deeply, composed myself, and dialed the number of Aspen Publishers in Rockville, Maryland. I accepted the invitation!

Previously, when asked if I intended to write a book based on my work, I'd say spiritedly, "Oh yes, I'm planning to. I definitely intend to. I'll get to it one day *real soon.*" So, although it may have seemed to be a hasty decision, the "birth" was due. I soon came to the realization that the timing was right for me as well as being synchronous with The United Nations Year of the Disabled Person. Three years later in 1985, *Music Therapy for the Developmentally Disabled* was published—a textbook used in colleges, universities, and music therapy programs in North America, South America, Europe, Asia, and Africa. To date there are translations in Italian and Korean, with Spanish and Japanese translations in progress.

During the writing of this textbook, Barbara Hesser, director of the New York University music therapy program, not only gave generously of herself as a consultant but also contributed a foreword that captures the spirit of what transpired in the music therapy room at MDC. I'm extremely pleased to say that our relationship—professional as well as personal—has resonated with deep and sonorous tones over the years. It was Barbara who was key in my being appointed to the faculty of New York University.

I JOIN THE FACULTY OF N.Y.U.

Before becoming a faculty member of N.Y.U., training and clinical supervision of interns were a basic feature of my program at MDC. Most of the interns assigned to serve their internship under my supervision. were in the N.Y.U. music therapy program. As a result of frequent on-site visits to observe her students and discuss their progress with me, Barbara became well-acquainted with my work as well as my background. Also, many students who were at different stages of their training in her program were given an open invitation to attend my sessions. What evolved was the next leap on my Tao as music therapist—appointment to the staff of the New York University music therapy program, initially as lecturer and subsequently as adjunct assistant professor. These years later, an archive of audio cassettes of my music therapy sessions at MDC has been made available to the students. Also, a scholarship in my name has been established.

A main concentration of my teaching has been as academic supervisor of interns. To date, in accordance with training guidelines of the American Association for Music Therapy (AAMT), the duties are threefold: (1) a seminar for the students who have reached the final stage of their training program, namely two consecutive semesters of internship at an accredited site where the intern receives direct clinical supervision, (2) two on-site observations per semester including three-way conferences with the clinical supervisor; and (3) individual conferences with the student. The variety of clients covered encompasses a broad range of disorders, conditions, and ages. It means being there for the intern who goes through a sweep of dichotomies: confidence and uncertainty, fulfillment and disappointment, self-assurance and self-doubt, enthusiasm and despair, success and failure, capability and inadequacy, joyous gratification and tearful chagrin, being effective and being fearful of doing harm, high self-esteem and low self-esteem, and so on. Sensitive, supportive handling is especially important at this critical time of the student's training.

MY COMMITMENT DEEPENS

Giving the course "Introduction to Music Therapy" was my initiation into "being on the other side of the desk" at New York University (as Dr. Jerrold Ross put it). I remember feeling that I was taking the exact step that I needed to at that time, and became immersed in assisting students find their identity in this modern profession that has deep roots in the tradition of healing through music. The challenge was not only to impart knowledge but to expand their awareness of the meaning and beauty of this treatment modality—to inspire and imbue them with the essence of what it is to be a music therapist.

This aspect of my Tao—teaching at New York University—has been exceptionally fulfilling and rewarding. I take great pride in being a part of a music therapy program, developed by Barbara Hesser, that is making such a valuable contribution to the training of music therapists. The humanistic philosophy that prevails is more than an academic exercise or intellectual concept. It is *actively* demonstrated by the warmth and humanity and caring and, yes, love, that make the program a most unusual university experience for all concerned. The faculty-student relationship is truly unique, and the ambiance that has evolved over the years is remarkably conducive to learning, to nurturing the human spirit, and to preparing for the challenges of the practice of the science and art of this discipline. The students in the music therapy program, with varying degrees of understanding of themselves and the field, make the choice to pursue a career in music therapy. I can say that all the students *truly want to be there*. Indeed, it is gratifying to teach in an environment where the students are more than willing and most often able!

The combination of teaching at New York University and practicing at MDC proved to be ideal. My roles as teacher and academic supervisor as well as clinical supervisor of interns placed me in the vantage point of offering training on many bases. I was able to dovetail and enrich my classes with both accounts of actual work with clients as well as make observations of my music therapy sessions available to the students. The interns in my seminar at N.Y.U. were placed in various sites under the supervision of different clinical supervisors, while I served as the academic supervisor of all of them and as both clinical and academic supervisor for those assigned to MDC.

To nurture therapists-to-be and to witness their growth is very much like guiding the process of their development, as Erik Erikson (1963) would put it, from infancy into a stage of autonomy. My approach to training the interns in both the art and science of conducting group and individual sessions has its focus in *A Continuum of Awareness*, the context I created for the practice of music therapy (as delineated in a subsequent chapter). Fostering and nurturing their unique identity musically and personally, I encourage them to explore and experiment with the therapeutic use of music of their particular heritage or preference—music they play and sing with ease, thus developing their own style, their individuality. This has given sessions an aliveness—a living quality—that is beneficial for both the interns and clients. Interns from diverse cultures and backgrounds have come to the profession offering music and genres that enrich the quality of the treatment and give a multicultural dimension to the musical environment: folk songs and indigenous music of students, for example, from Spain, the Philippines, Argentina, Israel, and China; the jazz idiom and pop songs of a performing musician; spirituals from the heritage of an African American; children's songs of a former kindergarten teacher; show tunes of an actor-singer. This self-exploratory stage is designed to prepare the interns to move from assisting me to trying out their own "voices" by conducting group and individual sessions independently. Once this inner musical being—this organic voice—is acknowledged or, as in some instances, *discovered* and then given outward expression, I have seen a shift in self-perception occur. The interns become more comfortable with themselves, more acquainted with who they are, more certain of relating to clients. Now on their way to developing their own style for making contact and establishing therapeutic relationships, they can then begin to deal with the clients' problems and conditions that need to be addressed and to respond to the here-and-now happenings of sessions. As they become more and more aware of this self-growth and get acknowledgment from me that it is "showing," a very special awakening takes place—an awakening to the possibility of actually *being* a music therapist.

I would often work at my desk in the music therapy room, keeping close watch over interns in their beginning ventures of the one-to-one treatment process. A particularly poignant example of the unexpected occurred at a session that an intern, Karen, was conducting. As both her N.Y.U. academic supervisor and clinical supervisor at MDC, I had guided her in finding her voice in the Negro spiritual genre. Consequently, she had already begun to establish a therapeutic relationship with eight-year-old Michael. Hyperactive and impulsive to an extreme, this young boy, in his earliest stages of development, had been deprived of contact with a mother figure.

Sitting on the floor opposite Michael, Karen sang softly, improvising words to the tune of the spiritual "Let My People Go." She sang, "Let's clap our hands to the music, clap clap clap clap, let's clap our hands to the music, and now we're going to stop." With the goal of impulse control by helping him internalize his ability to start and stop within the musical structure, Karen directed her uplifted hands gently toward Michael's. All was going well when suddenly I heard Karen cry out in pain. I looked up to see her struggling to extricate herself from Michael's grip. He had reached over, and with a look of utter joy, was vigorously pulling Karen's invitingly long hair.

Was Michael giving us a clue that he had not experienced one of an infant's most gratifying and loving expressions of intimacy with his mother—running his hands through his mother's hair? Was Michael filling in a missing stage of his growth and development? After soothing Karen's ruffled feelings (and hair) and without in any way making him "wrong," we immediately resolved the practical aspect of the situation by having Karen change her hairstyle to one not easily pulled. Then we showed Michael how to *stroke* Karen's hair to the tender strains of a rhythmic pattern, while she chanted and improvised words that identified and acknowledged what he was doing—a musical activity that brought smiles to his usually tense face. This was a mind-expanding learning experience for Karen.

At the N.Y.U. weekly internship seminar she related this incident to other interns who were in a variety of settings working with many different kinds of clients. The nature of the seminar is such that the students learn from each other and absorb what might ring true for them. We would explore meanings, implications, and specific music therapy techniques and strategies that were used—that could be applicable to the full spectrum of clients. I encouraged them to build upon their own hands-on work: to hone their ability to "think on their feet"; to acquire the skill and confidence to apply methods *spontaneously or extemporaneously* to meet the needs of the here-and-now client; to develop the capacity to combine intuition with effective mindful action.

But, as comprehensive as a training program may be, putting it into action—doing the "real thing"—is usually anxiety-provoking and calls for careful, caring guidance. This guidance, in addition to the above-mentioned features of the N.Y.U. internship, includes examination of the required daily internship logs. While reading these logs, I would often find myself making a comment such as: "The description of what you did is very clear. I can really get a sense of what your intention was. However, you don't identify any of the techniques or strategies that you used. *Do you know that you were using a specific music therapy technique there and a strategy there?*" And almost as often, the intern would answer with a puzzled yet secretly pleased, "I was!" Then, together we would ferret out the techniques and discuss them in relation to the demands and processes of particular sessions. This thoroughgoing evaluation is designed to raise awareness—to have the interns become cognizant of what they are doing, thus laying the foundation for working more consciously and effectively.

Third Movement

CREATING A CONTEXT FOR PRACTICE

The source of creation is . . . consciousness . . . pure
potentiality seeking expression from the
unmanifest to the manifest.

—Deepak Chopra

There are many ways to discover and rediscover
the sacredness and magic of human life. At heart,
all of these ways [reveal] human life as a journey
and as an adventure that has no end. The journey is
a quest for joining inner and outer experience,
mind and body, and waking up in the reality of
being genuinely human.

—Jeremy Hayward

ON MY HUMANISTIC CONNECTION

> . . . the human goal, the humanistic goal is
> ultimately the "self-actualization" of a person, the
> becoming fully human . . .
>
> — Abraham H. Maslow

From the very moment I entered the training program at New York University, the American Association for Music Therapy (AAMT) has played a dominant role in my life as music therapist. All along the way, its humanistic philosophical and psychological orientation have been an underpinning of the stance I have embraced as a therapist and as a human being.

A flood of thoughts and memories overtakes me at the realization that AAMT will not exist beyond 1997 when the two national organizations merge to become The American Music Therapy Association (AMTA). One of its original members, my Tao as a music therapist has run parallel to the combined existence of AAMT and its predecessor, The Urban Federation of Music Therapy. In 1974 I gave my first music therapy presentation at an AAMT conference. And, in 1995, twenty-one years later, I had the honor of being the first recipient of the AAMT Lifetime Achievement Award.

As I reexamine my commitment to AAMT (and its commitment to its members), an insight literally hits me between the eyes. Just as I knew on a deeply intuitive level at a certain juncture in my life that my Tao was to be a music therapist, I intuitively gravitated toward the national association that embodied the art and science of humanistic music therapy. It confirmed and affirmed my deepest yearnings for our species to consciously and mindfully—in the words of humanistic or "third force" psychologists—be concerned with love, spirit, creativity, emotional well-being, basic need gratification, self-growth, self-actualization, higher values, spontaneity, play, humor, affection, naturalness, warmth, autonomy, courage, responsibility, transcendence, peak experience. This regard for humanness and humaneness, for fostering more peaceable relations with others, for being and living on the highest levels that we are capable of, has given AAMT a unique place in the world of music therapy. I have felt truly "at home" with AAMT and secure in the conviction that my practice as a music therapist has put into action its life-giving concept and point of view.

And of vital importance, the warmth and camaraderie that pervades an AAMT conference or meeting, the genuine and mutual pleasure of sharing ideas and goings on—personal or professional, individual or collective—attest to the identity of our members. I can count among them loving friends and cherished colleagues.

Historically, my professional involvement goes back to the conference in 1974 when the vote to change the name from that of its predecessor, the Urban Federation of Music Therapy, to the American Association for Music Therapy took place. At this writing, I'm overcome by a mixture of joy and sadness—joy at having participated in AAMT's beginning in the world of music therapy and in its growth over its years of existence; sadness at witnessing its ending as a primary force in the field. l dwell on how my journey has intertwined with AAMT—serving on the board of directors, on the committee for education and training, being editor of our journal, *Music Therapy*, contributing to the newsletter, *Tuning In*, presenting at national conferences and at music therapy world congresses in Spain and Brazil, as well as representing AAMT at world congresses for the isolated/autistic child and for the developmentally disabled.

Our journal, *Music Therapy*, culls fond memories. This journal would mark the beginning of the second decade of AAMT. Barbara Hesser was to be editor. Recalling the first planning meeting, in the course of selecting a name several were tossed into the ring. After a discussion of pros and cons, I suggested, "Why not simply call it 'Music Therapy'?" There was full agreement. In the summer of 1981, the first volume of *Music Therapy* was issued.

I'm happy to say that my initial foray into the field of writing on the subject of music therapy entitled "A Continuum of Awareness: Music Therapy with the Developmentally Handicapped" appeared in that first volume. In 1987–88, I served a two-year term as editor. Creating a forum for expanding the scope of our field, I invited notable musicians as well as music therapists to write on the theme of music therapy and peace. The 1987 volume opens with the inspirational words of the revered Chilean poet, Pablo Neruda:

> I want to live in a world where beings are only human
> . . . I still have absolute faith in human destiny, a
> clearer and clearer conviction that we are approaching
> a great common tenderness . . . . At this critical
> moment . . . we know that the true light will enter
> those eyes that are vigilant. We shall all understand
> one another. We shall advance together. (1987)

The volume closes with my "Song of Peace for the Children."

Now in 1997, I have written an article for the last issue of *Music Therapy.* The last issue! That is heart wrenching. So intimately involved in the importance of our journal and its special contribution to the field of music therapy, I was hard put to believe it would no longer exist. However, its spirit will continue on and on . . . Contemplating on the cyclical character of beginnings, endings, and new beginnings of my Tao, and seeing it reflected in the beginning and ending of AAMT and the beginning of a new association, I take comfort in the fact that music therapists of the United States will function together on newfound levels. This exit at the turn of the century and entrance into the next millennium holds boundless opportunities and possibilities for the future of our field. And, just as the indomitable spirit of *Music Therapy* will continue to have a strong impact on the quality and nature of the new journal, so the humanistic viewpoint and invincible spirit of AAMT will continue to influence the quality and nature of the work of music therapists globally.

Note: An added organizational dimension to my humanistic connection is with the Association for Humanistic Psychology (AHP), founded by Abraham Maslow and Anthony J. Sutich in

1958. A member of this organization, I was invited in 1976 to write an article for the *Journal of Humanistic Psychology* and, as founder-director of Music Therapists for Peace, contributed to an annual conference on conflict resolution.

A CONTINUUM OF AWARENESS IS THE CONTEXT

> A continuum is something whose parts are so close
> together. . . that the continuum cannot be broken
> down into them. . . . It is called a continuum
> because it flows continuously.
>
> — Gary Zukov

> The experientialists . . . see that in the center of life
> is the means of communication namely, awareness.
>
> — Frederick S. Perls

The concept of *A Continuum of Awareness* is intrinsic to my journey as a person and music therapist, and to the journeys of persons I treat. It was not until I was actually in training to become a certified music therapist that this context and concept of experiencing "awareness" and "consciousness" and "aware consciousness" and "conscious awareness" on their many levels became basic to my treatment methodology. I found that we are all a part of the same consciousness—a universal consciousness; that our differences are just a matter of levels, or planes. Being alive presupposes that we are experiencing. But is it aware or unaware experiencing? This distinction was brought home sharply when I began to work with a diversity of developmentally disabled persons who lack, in varying degrees, awareness of self, others, and the environment. Treatment based in the context of *A Continuum of Awareness* is designed to awaken, heighten, and expand conscious awareness.

Although I worked for thirteen years with hundreds of developmentally disabled persons of all ages and conditions, it was upon the first encounters in my path as a music therapist with three very different autistic children, Darryl, Kathy, and Margarita that I conceived the context of my approach to the practice of music therapy, I seem to have had a sense of who they were, what their needs were, and how their inner beings were to be cared for through the extraordinary treatment of music therapy. This knowing defies intellectual explanation. It combines intangibles with tangibles: empathic, intuitive, compassionate humanness with action that is rooted in the conscious use of the power of music.

What emanated from this insight was not only the certainty that being a music therapist was my Tao, but that the nature of my contribution to the field of music therapy evolved from a deep-seated desire to reach the unreachable human being.

The fundamental connection between being reachable and having an awareness of being a Self came through to me with crystal-clear impact. The realization that it very likely stemmed from my own need as a young child to be reached, to be a Self, was startling and tremendously enlightening. It was not accidental (as I have said before, there are no accidents!) that during my music therapy training I had begun to investigate at what age self-awareness begins to evolve in the young child—that this was the topic of a paper I chose to write for a course in child psychology. The study led to the assumption that self-awareness "normally" begins to manifest around the second year, and at that developmental stage comes the beginnings of awareness of others and the environment. The sense of Self is essential.

The evolvement of the context of *A Continuum of Awareness* went through much experimentation, discovery, and experiential trial. Although the main focus of its application in this book is with persons who are diagnosed as developmentally disabled, this paradigm is applicable to all client populations, is practiced around the world, and goes beyond the treatment room out to all people. On a continuum, it has expanded to the work of Music Therapists for Peace and Students Against Violence Everywhere—S.A.V.E. through Music Therapy (as discussed in the Fifth Movement).

A CONTINUUM OF AWARENESS EXPLICATED

I have been fired by the notion that when we humans grasp the idea that we *are* consciousness, that being alive *is* consciousness, then *the experiencing of conscious awareness on the many levels of existence becomes natural—effortless.* The implications and significance of this assumption are powerful. I thought, "What could be more fitting than an approach to music therapy that focuses on cultivating awareness?" An approach that holds this premise as well as promise deals with the whole person—mentally, emotionally, physically, psychosocially. It has the potential to tap into the wellness of the person: to effect states of aliveness, to enhance the ability to communicate and function more fully in life. Interestingly enough, this approach not only sharpens the client's awareness, it sharpens the therapist's awareness as well!

My first experience as a practicing music therapist propelled me directly into creating this context. The awareness of the child who has early childhood autism is "conspicuously lacking"—so extreme that *self-awareness* may be totally lacking. "How," I asked myself, "can I find ways to assist the child to develop a sense of Self, to become aware of the immediate environment, to relate to and communicate with other human beings?" The search was on.

The actual term *A Continuum of Awareness* originated with the father of modern Gestalt Therapy, Frederick (Fritz) S. Perls (1976). Having absorbed the philosophy and practice of this psychotherapy which is succinctly summarized in the Perls quote at the beginning of the chapter, I adopted and adapted it as the context of my approach to music therapy. Paradoxically this context is at once elemental yet complex: elemental in its underlying concept and complex in its all-encompassing perspective. *It is not only applicable to children with autism and other persons with developmental disabilities but to all people including the so-called "normal."* In that light, let us travel into this realm together.

THE CONCEPT: A NONLINEAR CONTINUUM

A continuum by its very nature is a nonlinear process with no beginning or end. Rather, it enfolds and unfolds on many levels simultaneously or progressively, defying measurement by charts or diagrams. *Awareness* exists as well as differs on these many levels in the same person—in various situations, at various times of day, from moment to moment—and, for that matter, at the same time! As with a continuum, awareness defies measurement although it can be observed, assessed, and assumed objectively via actions, behaviors, and acquired skills, and consciously experienced subjectively via a range of feelings, energy, and emotions. Qualitative changes, sometimes even transformations, occur as a result of a shift of perception. In Gestaltian terms, this shift, which has no quantifiable time frame, can take place in a flash as a result of a cycle of awareness-excitement-contact (Zinker, 1978). The cycle can be generated by internal or external sensations triggered by auditory or visual or kinesthetic stimuli.

THE PERSPECTIVE: "MUSIC THERAPY FOR LIVING"

In the philosopher Suzanne Langer's view, key to the significance that music has in our lives is its *congruence* with human emotions and feelings (1942). It is this congruence that can effect immediate contact as a multisensory stimulant physiologically and psychologically, and give impetus to the awakening, heightening, and expanding of the awareness continuum. The goal is to motivate purposeful and positive actions and to ultimately have us become "as aware as possible of the effect of our actions" (May, 1972).

I have come to call the holistic perspective of *A Continuum of Awareness*, "Music Therapy for Living." As the term implies, the principle of awareness embraces the spectrum of living. Once I established the framework/context of my approach, I needed to trust my intuition to guide me in putting it into actual practice. For one thing, the music therapy process is not restricted to scheduled sessions. I have intentionally arranged to be with clients in many different circumstances of their lives: in their living quarters, in their homes, at concerts, at restaurants, on walks, at dental and medical visits, and so on. And, because sessions may not always follow the planned schedule or be conducted under "ideal" circumstances, I sensed the importance of liberating myself from commonly accepted constraints or parameters or conventions of "the session." Living situations that would ordinarily be considered an interruption—for example, while with clients the telephone rings or while conducting a session with a patient in a hospital setting a nurse rushes in to perform a routine check-up—can be skillfully and humanly incorporated into the process.

The practice of the art and science of this approach involves training as well as an attitude that is conducive to it. Professors tell of the response that students have upon learning about it. Music therapists who have either trained with me or have made a study of this approach through my textbook and course work give testimony that it has deeper and deeper meaning for them over the years. Reports give evidence of the benefits to *both the client and the therapist.*

THREE MAIN STRATEGIES

It was in the very first encounters with autistic children, mentioned previously, that I was aware that special means of reaching them would be required—were, in fact, essential; that innovative strategies specifically designed to address their unique behaviors and problems needed to be created. In essence, the three main strategies I devised for making contact with the unreachable child—*Reflection, Identification,* and *Our Contact Song*—grew organically out of the need to bring about a human relationship that would make treatment possible.

Of these terms that I have chosen to designate the strategies, Reflection and Identification appear in the English language and psychotherapeutic systems in different ways, for different purposes, and with different meanings. Their meaning In this context is described below. Our Contact Song, however, is an original term—a term whose usage and meaning apply exclusively to the third strategy devised for my approach to music therapy.(It is important to note here that these strategies and the concept of A Continuum of Awareness have broad application—not only to persons who have disorders or disabilities but to the average or normal population.)

Seemingly conceived intuitively or in moments of inspired spontaneity, in actuality these strategies were the result of (1) a thorough investigation of the mystery of this condition and its baffling symptoms; (2) research into the nature of awareness and self-awareness; and (3) engagement with and study of the children themselves. But that is not the whole story. How did these strategies originate? What is their source, their roots?

Both Reflection and Identification had beginnings in my early days of motherhood, and I venture to say emanated from an empathic quality that seems to be primal in many parents. For, when I came face to face with finding ways to make contact with another human being on the simplest, most elementary nonverbal levels, I thought back to my days as a mother of infants. How did I make contact through sound? Yes, I talked and sang and played music morning, noon, and night, constantly creating a stimulating "sound" environment. I had serious fun with the sounds and gestures that I as a mother made instinctively when reflecting or mirroring—*never mimicking*—the baby's sounds and facial expressions and movements. Having studied the theories of child psychologist Jean Piaget, I was aware of the various developmental stages from the earliest cooing, babbling, lallation, vocalizations, and on to first words. It was delicious being there for my children, teaching them in a most enjoyable way, watching them develop a sense of self and others, letting them know that I was receiving and responding to their communications. I find this carryover to the future exciting to contemplate.

These years later as I thoroughly investigated humanistic psychologists and psychotherapists, I was already attuned to the therapeutic technique that Carl Rogers (1971) based his entire approach to client-centered psychotherapy on, namely Reflection. It is no wonder that when creating A Continuum of Awareness, the very first strategy for this paradigm presented itself in the form of an adaptation of Rogers' technique to musical improvisational forms of reflecting/mirroring. That mysterious kind of knowing engulfed me. I *knew* how to go about establishing contact by awakening awareness of self—who and what the client is. I *knew* that unconditional acceptance and regard matched the core of my being. And taking that strategy to another dimension, I devised Identification as a means to further awaken and expand awareness. In some instances, it becomes necessary to be the alter ego of a person whose capacity to express the here-and-now happenings are limited or nonexistent. The significance of *Our Contact Song,* which the name itself reveals, has warranted a separate chapter.

A digest of the strategies is as follows:

REFLECTION: an adaptation of the Carl Rogers' psychotherapeutic technique to the music therapy process, is instantaneous playback of vocal, instrumental, or gestural expression and responses of the here-and-now person structured by the music therapist into musical forms: rhythmic chants, improvised songs, instrument playing, and movement.

The quintessential purpose for mirroring/matching what the person is doing or not doing is the unconditional acceptance and regard that genuinely acknowledges who the person is. The awakening and heightening of awareness engendered by this kind of attention and respect from another can effect a positive change in one's perception of self. Concerning destructive, harmful, or pain-inflicting behaviors to self or others, awareness is promoted through identification not reflection.

IDENTIFICATION: instantaneous feedback of the here-and-now person and what is happening in the environment, *identifying* in improvised words of song and rhythmic chants who we are, what the person is doing or not doing, what we are doing together. It is a dimension that not only serves to awaken awareness but raises it to higher levels. For clients who are not verbal, the therapist becomes their alter ego rendering meaning and focus to what is occurring, thus enhancing conscious experiencing. Those who are verbal are encouraged and helped to take an active role in this process, singing or chanting along with the therapist or in response to the therapist's prompts. The experimentation and exploration in which the therapist and client are existentially engaged is a way of getting to know each other. It deepens and gives added scope to the therapeutic relationship, often leading to the discovery of Our Contact Song.

OUR CONTACT SONG: a composed or improvised song, the first musical expression *initiated by the client* and received by the therapist that indicates awareness of and a link with another. The discovery of this special song may involve numerous musical and emotional experiences—trials and frustrations, moments of failure and joy. Once discovered, it becomes a catalyst for the first *two-way communication,* and although there may have been response to other music that the therapist has played or sung, actual contact is made when the client spontaneously gives this sign of awareness. The song may be one that the therapist intuitively or consciously selects based on an aspect or interest of the person, or one that the person has an attachment to or an affinity for. Best a song that lends itself to improvisational variations and adaptations, it becomes a fountainhead for myriad experiences and activities in the service of therapeutic goals.

These three strategies lay the foundation for intrinsic (internalized) learning and intentional action. Coexisting and co-experiencing, the client and therapist journey together into A Continuum of Awareness as illustrated in the Fourth Movement.

An added note about Reflection, the strategy that initiates the continuum: It is a verbal as well as nonverbal means of contact and communication that people use naturally without being aware of it. In addition, the multicultural world that we live in necessitates that we develop the ability to relate to people whose languages are other than one's own. Used in this way, reflection is pivotal in helping deal with the immediate and far-flung multicultural environments: the therapist is able to make contact with people of diverse languages and cultures.

Two dissimilar instances are striking examples of its "living" quality. One relates to the film, "Walkabout" whose theme revolves around an Australian aboriginal young boy who is engaged in the rite of passage to manhood. On his "walkabout" through the Outback, he encounters two young Australian girls from the upper strata of Australian society who, on a trip with their father, were separated from him and have lost their way. They meet up with the Aboriginal boy and not only don't understand his language but are fearful of him. Attempts to understand each other cause tension to arise between them. Finally, there is a dramatic moment when the boy begins to make contact by instinctively reflecting what the two girls are saying. It is then that they lose their fear of this stranger and are able to understand each other enough to make it possible for the boy to help them find the way back to their father. I leaned toward the person I was with (who happened to be a music therapist) and excitedly whispered, "Do you realize what just happened? That was a perfect example of Reflection! It's an affirmation of the 'living truth' of this strategy." She nodded enthusiastically.

Another instance took place in a family hotel in Argentina where only Spanish was spoken. After dinner, many of the guests gathered in the main sitting room where there was a grand piano. As I started to play, parents and their children clustered around the piano. Wanting to make contact with them, I started to improvise on the keyboard and reflect vocally the children's sounds and words. Sparks of energy flew back and forth! We were enjoying human loving contact, then fell to playing and singing "Sing" from *The Sesame Street Song Book* (1971) At the end of each verse comes a section of joyous and rhythmic singing of the universal syllable "la." Exaggerating and articulating the syllable very clearly, even the youngest of the children were able to reflect/mirror the rhythmic patterns of the melodic line. The spirit of this joyful note transcended the language barrier. We were human beings brought together through music, no longer strangers.

Similar experiences took place in Haiti, Brazil, Spain, and Russia.

FROM MY HEART: OUR CONTACT SONG

> It was my songs that taught me all the lessonsI ever learnt. They showed me secret paths; they brought before my sight many a star onthe horizon of my heart.
>
> —Rabindranath Tagore

> Song is the noblest, the most intimate, the mostcomplete manner of self-expression known to mankind, and in the last analysis self-expressionis the great thing for which mankind is ever searching. . . . There comes into every life a time when. . .the soul craves that which it can supply to itself alone. . . . Song then becomes not only . . . a solace but also an inspiration.
>
> — Oscar Saenger in William H. Calvin,
> *The Cerebral Symphony: Seashore Reflections on the Structure of Consciousness*

It would seem that the mysterious ways of circular time that Michael Talbot boggles the mind with in his *Holographic Universe* (1994) were subtly unfolding here. Ever since my high school days I wrote poetry, and in college wrote classical songs (one set to a poem of Shelly). In 1961, entering a renewed songwriting phase of my musical evolution, I wrote a song to the poetry of Emily Dickinson (an idol for whom I romantically named my daughter) entitled "Without You," and another inspired both by a Paul Gauguin painting and Paul Robeson's rich voice (two idols for

BIRD OF LIGHT

Words and Music by
Edith Hillman Boxill

Fly to the North,——— To the South East and West,———

Then fold your wings,——— And——— as you rest,———

Bird of Light sing a-gain,——— Bird of Light sing a-gain,———

sing with a sound that is clear and bright. Bird of

Bird of Light sing of peace,____ Bird of Light sing of peace,____

Sing so that war will for - e - ver cease, Bird of Peace,

Bird   of Peace,   Bird   of Peace.

whom I romantically named my son) entitled "Look Over Yonder." In the same period, I wrote "Bird"—a song that has interwoven itself into my life in a way that helps makes sense of the holographic nature of our existence. Written many years back, it has held a uniquely emotion-filled place in my heart and is viewed as Our Contact Song. It is the song I wrote for my daughter Emily and son Paul that started out as "Bird." and went through several transformations before it became "Bird of Light."

The dedication of the original song "Bird" is:

To Emily who *is* an adorable little bird,

and

To Paul who *heard* birds singing last night . . .

The original lyrics, written in 1961, are as follows:

BIRD

Oh bird of my delight, sing to me, sing to me,
Oh bird of my delight, sing to me, sing to me,
Sing with a sound that is clear and bright,
Oh sweetest bird of my delight.

Oh bird of my delight, sing of love, sing of love,
Oh bird of my delight, sing of love, sing of love,
Sing with a heart that is clear and bright,
Oh sweetest bird of my delight.

Fly 'round and 'round
Spread your wings free and wide
Fly to the sky.
Fly, fly, fly.
Fly to the North,
South, East, and West,
Fly to the sky,
And as you fly . . .
Oh bird of my delight, sing again, sing again,
Oh bird of my delight, sing again, sing again,
Sing your song of love day and night,
Oh sweetest bird of my delight.

The first transformation in 1978, both musically and textually, brought it to a new spiritual level:

BIRD OF LIGHT

Bird of Light, sing to me,
Bird of Light, sing to me,
Sing with a sound that is clear and bright,
Bird of Light.

Bird of Light, sing of love,
Bird of Light, sing of love,
Open your heart and let it take flight,
Bird of Light.

Fly 'round and 'round,
Spread your wings far and wide,
Fly to the sky, Fly, fly, fly,
Fly to the North, to the South, East, and West,
Then fold your wings, and as you rest . . .

Bird of Light, sing again,
Bird of Light, sing again,
Sing with a sound that is clear and bright,
Bird of Light.

The verse added in 1985 is a plea for energy and strength:

Bird of Light, shine on me,
Bird of Light, shine on me,
Shine with a light that is strong and bright,
Bird of Light.

The most recent transformation in 1988 was inspired at the time of my founding of Music Therapists for Peace:

Bird of Light sing of peace,
Bird of Light sing of peace,
Sing so that war will forever cease,
Bird of Peace . . . Bird of Peace . . . Bird of Peace . . . Root

ROOT SOURCES OF OUR CONTACT SONG

The concept of the strategy Our Contact Song was taking root in me as far back as the birth of my children, Paul and Emily. For, although the theoretical basis was to be formulated through my work as a music therapist many years hence, the germ of the idea had its natural organic beginnings in my early days of motherhood and "doing music" with two- to five-year olds—including my own two children—at The Bank Street Nursery School.

When I was offered the position to be the *music person* there, I was positively enthralled by the idea of doing music with children the same age as my own children—of sharing the music that we so loved and was so interwoven into our beings. Now I would make music time at the nursery school fun time, going-to-sleep/nap time, birthday party time, holiday time, sharing time.

So there we were: one child in the "young twos" and the other in the "young fives," their mother the music person, and their father the attending pediatrician who had the "fun" of looking down all the children's throats every morning as they walked in (or were carried in). Was this combined "family service" of meeting the health and musical needs of children another development foretelling my future? Was it a precursor of my Tao as a music therapist? Photographs of my music sessions at Bank Street that turned up recently are graphic indicators that my journey had already taken this direction.

A mother and musician, I was very much aware of how songs create a powerful bond between mother and child—how songs evoke a sensitive, tender, precious contact that is theirs and theirs alone. In addition to the many songs I sang to and with my children, there was a particular one that each child connected to emotionally. The following incidents illustrate the conditions under which these special songs were the catalyst for the idea of Our Contact Song, and, all important, how the emotional linkage that evolved from these special songs became a decisive factor in their purpose and use—indispensable lessons I learned along the way.

How fascinating it is to observe one's selective memories and the meaning we attribute to them. Coming directly from my heart are two especially relevant and revealing musical experiences. Improvising songs and drawing upon my ever-growing repertoire of folk songs, I also improvised and adapted words of songs in the oral tradition of the folk-song idiom. These were

natural ways of being totally in the present with the age groups divided into young and old twos or threes or fours or fives.

One cheerful April morning, for the first time in this setting I introduced the traditional Southern action song, "Up On the Mountain" to the group that Paul was in—the young fives. This song had become a particular favorite at home and, in retrospect, had taken on the quality of Our Contact Song. The words we sang at home were in the collection of songs and musical games, *Songs to Grow On* (1950).

I opened the activity with those words:

> Up on the mountain, two by two,
> Up on the mountain, two by two,
> Up on the mountain, two by two,
> Rise, sugar, rise.
>
> Let me see you make a motion, two by two,
> Let me see you make a motion, two by two,

"Up on the Mountain" Music here

UP ON THE MOUNTAIN

Traditional American Folk Song

G
D7
Up on the mountain, two by two, Up on the mountain, two by two,
G
D7
G
Up on the mount-ain, two by two, Rise, su-gar, rise.
G
Let me see you make a mo-tion, two by two, Let me
D7
G
see you make a mo-tion, two by two, Let me see you make a
D7
G
mo-tion, two by two, Rise su-gar, rise.

> Let me see you make a motion, two by two,
> Rise, sugar, rise.
>
> That's a very fine motion, 'deed it is,
> That's a very fine motion, 'deed it is,
> That's a very fine motion, 'deed it is,
> Rise, sugar, rise.

Then I began to improvise words:

> Let's walk around the room, two by two,
> Let's walk around the room, two by two,
> Let's walk around the room, two by two,
> Holding hands together . . .
>
> Now let's make a motion, two by two.
> Now let's make a motion, two by two,
> Now let's make a motion, two by two,
> Holding hands together.
>
> That's a very good motion, Cindy and Paul,
> That's a very good motion Cindy and Paul,
> That's a very good ——

Suddenly Paul started to run out of the room, obviously troubled.

In retrospect, it is hard to believe that I hadn't realized that singing different words from those *belonging to us* would cause confusion in his young mind. Bringing him back into the room and having him sit close by my side, I immediately began to sing the song as he knew it. He regained his usual sunny self as he heard words that were familiar to him. In viewing this happening in the context of my Tao as a music therapist, it takes on a distinct meaning that is truly mind-boggling. I stumbled inadvertently but directly onto a crucial lesson!

And, what took place on a hot, sticky summer's day when Emily was a year-and-a half young pointed up a knowing that I felt was rooted in my psyche but had never before directly experienced in this particular way. During her afternoon nap I thought to get some relief from the heat by pinning my shoulder-length hair in an upswing hairstyle. However, when I went to lift her out

MY DARLING

of her crib, she looked at me and began to cry. Her eyes asked, "Who is this stranger? Where is my mother?" I was chagrined. What had I done to cause this outburst? A second later, I realized that visually I was not the mother she was familiar with. Holding her close to me, I quickly made contact with her by singing a song that I had written especially for her—a tender lullaby, "My Darling"—a song I had sung to her many times improvising words to suit the moment:

> Emily is my darling,
> Emily is my darling,
> Emily is my darling,
> Yes she is, she is.

> Emily, I love you,
> Emily, I love you,
> Emily, I love you,
> Yes I do, I do.

As I sang this song over and over and then others that she had heard me sing time and again, her crying subsided. Smiling and hugging me, she called out, "Mommy." "Yes, Emmy, yes, Emmy," I said joyously. "I'm Mommy." All was well with the world again.

ANOTHER LOOK AT OUR CONTACT SONG

I had been the supervisor of a student, Maria Elena Lopez, in the New York University music therapy program. After graduating, she would often come to visit with me both for professional and personal guidance. We would share ideas about music therapy generally as well as discuss problems that she was facing at an institution for developmentally disabled adults. And we shared enjoyable moments of singing and music making as well. One song that she especially loved was "Bird of Light."

Using the strategies of *A Continuum of Awareness* in her work, Maria Eléna was well versed in the concept of Our Contact Song, and inasmuch as "Bird of Light" was a source of congruent feelings at our "sessions," we agreed, with a sense of playfulness, that it had become Our Contact Song. However, it was to take on a more serious note.

As we finished the song at one session, we looked at each other in a moment of silence. Then in her charming Argentine accent Maria Eléna said. "Edith, I have something to ask you—*I would like you to be my mother.*" Without a moment's hesitation, my answer was a warm embrace. At the time, I thought it was a touching affirmation of the bond that was developing between us. Some time later I learned that she had suffered the loss of her mother in a tragic accident in Argentina. We have developed a mother-daughter kinship that has grown closer and deeper over the years.

That "Bird of Light" has been Our Contact Song in its broadest sense has been in ongoing evidence. It has become our greeting for each other in person, by telephone, in letters, wherever we are. And not least, a professional relationship developed that has been enormously rewarding. We have given lectures at Argentine universities, presentations at world congresses, workshops in Buenos Aires, Posadas, Rio de Janeiro, and the United States. As the international coordinator of Music Therapists for Peace since its inception, Maria Eléna has been expanding our work through television and radio, at community events, and at national and international conferences in the United States and Argentina At this writing, she is arranging a Music Therapists for Peace Congress to take place in Argentina in August of 1988. She is truly an "ambassador of peace" through music therapy, sending the message of MTP and the healing sounds of our Peace Bell through South America.

"Bird of Light" has had special meaning throughout my life. Clearly, it has been a Contact Song that has worked its magic in personal ways, first with my children and then with my grandchildren. And in music therapy sessions.
Yes, "Bird of Light' has flown to many parts of the globe, making loving contact on every flight.

FOURTH MOVEMENT

THE MIRACLE IN ACTION

The highest attitude toward individual differences
is to be aware of them, to accept them, but also to
enjoy them and finally be profoundly grateful for
them as a beautiful instance of the ingenuity of the
cosmos—the recognition of their value, and
wonder at individual differences ... the
recognition of the essential commonness and
mutual belongingness and identification with all
kinds of people in ultimate humanness or
spescieshood ...
—Abraham H. Maslow

The greatest insight, thought and art concerning
the humancondition and its divine aspirations are
rooted in thephenomenon of inner vision.

—José and Miriam Arguelles

PEEKING THROUGH A ONE-WAY MIRROR

> Of all psychology's sins, the mostmortal is its
> neglect of beauty. Thereis, after all, something quite
> beautifulabout a life.
>
> — James Hillman

GETTING TO KNOW YOU

As is every human being, the developmentally disabled person is
a unique individual and personality. And, as with all human beings, there lies within a healthy self. This healthy self may lie
dormant, waiting—sometimes patiently, sometimes impatiently—
to be discovered, uncovered, nurtured.

Music has miraculous effects on the human organism. I
have veritably jumped for joy at a spontaneous response to the
music therapy process from one who *seemed* to be oblivious of
what was going on. The inherent elements of music—its rhythm,
melody, tempo, dynamics, timbre/tonal colors, song texts—are
powerful means of contacting and activating the inner being on
multiple levels. And, constantly on the alert for even the most
minimal signs of contact, I assist the person to, perhaps for the
first time, give outward expression—to vocalize or sing or move
to the music or use a simple musical instrument. *These are the
moments when we begin our journey together.*

The varying degrees of severity and kinds of developmental disabilities,* very often compounded by emotional disturbance cause major deficits in the capacity to communicate in the broadest sense: vocalizations, verbalizations, speech, and purposeful body gestures. Interpersonal relations are limited, in some instances nonexistent. Establishing a trusting client-therapist relationship and fostering the person's awareness of self, others, and the environment are fundamental.

Strengths and interests are all-important gauges of potential growth and improvement. We put no ceilings on the possibilities. And, although assessment and evaluation of functioning levels—developmental, psychological, behavioral, cognitive, physical, and psychosocial—provide a basis for treatment, *we must never lose sight of the whole person.*

There is empirical evidence that music therapy for developmentally disabled persons has not only proved to be a primary treatment modality but, as the pioneering work of Paul Nordoff and Clive Robbins informs us (1971), can be an aid to diagnosis. And, adding dimension to the music therapy process, I reinforce, supplement, and incorporate goals of speech therapy, occupational therapy, physical therapy, and special education through interdisciplinary work.

My approach—the paradigm of *A Continuum of Awareness*—is wholistic. Changes in awareness, shifts in perception, transformations in functioning that show up as expressive action are guiding lights and telling signals that the therapy is "taking."

You are now invited to look in on some miracles. . . .

---

* The five categories of developmental disabilities are: mental retardation, autism, cerebral palsy, epilepsy, and neurological impairment.

DARRYL: MUSIC THERAPY UNDER A DESK

Music therapy under a desk? What was that all about? What would the director of the Manhattan Children's Treatment Center have thought?

Baffling. Puzzling. Yes, the autistic child is still an enigma. From the earliest stages of infancy, the child appears to be alien to the human world. Most often physical growth takes a healthy course. However, the usual awareness of a differentiated self does not develop and there is *apparent* unawareness of "I"—his or her own identity and of "you" another person. Receptive and expressive means of communication are severely disturbed, or in the extreme, completely unavailable. Activated largely by self-stimulation and preoccupied with inanimate objects, the child is involuted—the nuances of emotive life inaccessible or obscure, lying hidden and secret behind the "autistic barrier." And so, behavior is bewildering, unpredictable, unfathomable, and although hearing and vision may be intact, acuity may be "short-circuited" and sensory perception noticeably distorted, highly selective, or cut off. There may be a sudden outburst of anguished self-abuse emanating from what appears to be an internal explosion, but no awareness of a blow inflicted by another child. There may be utter oblivion to a clash of cymbals but visible shrinking from the sound of a soft voice calling to them. There may be "splinter" displays of phenomenal feats of memory, but no recognition of his or her own name. Pain but no tears, play but no laughter.

The autistic child, although a unique individual, shares with other autistic children a most telling and observable characteristic—the inward look of eyes that "defy" contact with another human being. Among the symptoms of this condition (eighteen of which were identified in 1943 by child psychiatrist Dr. Leo Kanner) are: lack of contact with other human beings; inability to communicate by ordinary means of verbal language; bizarre behaviors and ritualistic mannerisms such as finger wiggling or touching a series of objects; preoccupation with inanimate objects; autoeroticisms or self-stimulation; need for sameness; self-inflicted bodily injury; and, "psychic" deafness and blindness. If there is speech, it is oftentimes echolalic (repetition of another's verbal communications), or idiosyncratic (unintelligible utterances peculiar to a person, either singly or in an outpouring of a stream of sounds). And although renowned investigators such as Leo

Kanner, Bernard Rimland, Lorna Wing, and Hans Asperger have for over fifty years zealously sought to discover the etiology of early infantile autism, the underlying causes remain a mystery. Lorna Wing (1974), an English child psychiatrist who has specialized in the study and treatment of autistic children, would have us look at the child rather than the diagnostic label. (I am in complete accord with her.) She also maintains that there has been no evidence that traditional psychotherapies have been effective with autistic children, mainly because these therapies are based on verbalization which is conspicuously lacking in the autistic child.

If verbal therapies are not efficacious, and if, as authorities in the field have reported, the autistic child has been found to be especially sensitive to musical sound, it follows that a more successful means of assistance may be found in a nonverbal treatment modality such as music therapy. Using music as a therapeutic agent—as a means of establishing contact with the autistic child, the music therapist can make available to the child who has no speech or whose speech is limited to echolalia, preverbal and nonverbal means of communication—"organic" sounds and vocalizations, emotional responses, bodily movements and gestures—all transformed and translated into musical forms. These forms can express the full human spectrum of feelings as well as the actual experiences of the here-and-now child. They are among the many paths that the music therapist can explore to help the child reach out to the external world and to other human beings.

There is much in the process of "giving the child to her/himself"—finding the "I." It is not easy to make contact with one whose eyes look away from or through you, who does not *seem* to hear you, who retreats from you by lapsing into what *appears* to be involuntary—perhaps defensive—mannerisms, or eludes you by "resorting" to self-stimulation. You have to literally burrow your way into the child's inner world. However, once contact is established, once the child has given a signal—a grunt, a glance, a touch, a rebuff, a smile, a punch— that she/he recognizes that you are there, the beginnings of interaction, minimal as they may seem, call for acknowledgment, caring response, and tender nurturing. In my experience, as soon as the young person begins to trust her or his own "feelers" of communication by being made aware that these bits and pieces are received by another, a shift in perception and actions can take place in a flash.

Before telling Darryl's story, I wish to make known my position on the so-called atypical child. An atypical child is a person, not merely a case or a patient or a client—a child who has "problems in living." I am another person—a music therapist who gives service (from the Greek *theraps*), one who coexists and coexperiences and interexperiences with the child, one who, in the initial stages, existentially may become an alter ego, empathically reflecting (Reflection) and identifying (Identification), the shared experiences, supportively nourishing and leading the child on A Continuum of Awareness toward the highest degree of autonomy possible. I learn about and study the child's particular condition and constantly tune into the here-and-now unique person. The nature and quality of the work is improvisational (Bruscia,1987).

When I started treating Darryl at the Manhattan Children's Treatment Center—a facility for emotionally disturbed children—on Ward's Island, he was an extremely attractive, somewhat undersized young boy of eleven. Except when engaged in autistic activity, such as spinning a spinnable object or resisting another person's attention, his assertive energy was at a low level, his arms hanging flaccidly by his side, unresponsive to human touch in contrast to the strength and motoric skills with which he handled objects. His legs and feet moved lifelessly except when spinning himself around, the epitome of a human top. And Darryl is echolalic. When I sang, pointing to him, "You are Darryl" and pointing to myself, "I am Edi," he echoed my words in a parrotlike manner with no inflection, "You are Darryl, I am Edi."

The staff of the special education program, including the music therapist, were having a difficult time handling Darryl's "bizarre" behaviors, particularly his frantic episodes' and withdrawal from contact with other children and his teacher. Lost in his own world, he was left pretty much to his own devices, a circumstance which caused him to be often in a state of turmoil and anguish. When I arrived on the scene, Jerry Schell, the music therapist at this facility, candidly told me that Darryl's condition was of such a nature that he didn't fit into any of the music therapy groups.

Since Darryl would run as often as he could to the music room and immerse himself in playing around with various instruments, Mr. Schell hoped that individual music sessions might possibly be an answer to Darryl's needs. I had had many years' experience doing music with children in many different kinds of

school settings. Therefore, although I was just beginning my training as a music therapist, my extensive experience with "typical" children (as well as with my daughter and son) was thought to be excellent preparation for this new work with an "atypical." child. Darryl was the first child with "a problem in living" (Szaaz, 1974) that I would be contacting through music.

With a sense that I was in the right place at the right time, I "took on" Darryl. He touched a deep chord in me. I felt that I knew him—knew who he was, knew what his needs were, knew what he was seeking to express. I was truly filled with the challenge of learning to serve this troubled child, figuring out what and how to contribute to his well-being. When his music therapy sessions started, the entire staff (including the director and the social worker) sighed with relief, and as the trusting relationship that evolved became known, there was many an instance when I was called on a "rescue mission" for Darryl.

As treatment progressed, I used a variety of music and songs, different instruments, and music-movement activities, all with the intention of freeing the flow of energy and expressivity that seemed to be crying for release. My client-therapist relationship with Darryl is one of the most memorable of my music therapy experience. Not only did I effect a critical change in Darryl, he effected a critical change in me.

When I consulted with his teacher to find out if she knew of any Darryl's interests, musically or otherwise, she answered, "Oh yes, I think he likes the song, 'Pop! Goes the Weasel.' " Well, that offered a possible clue in the work with Darryl. I saw the potential for using it in any number of ways to make initial contact with him and to establish rapport. At the next session, I began to sing and play it on the autoharp. Lo and behold, I detected him humming the melody under his breath. And then, as I continued to sing I caught an almost inaudible singing of the words "Pop! Goes the Weasel." How fantastic. Did we have Our Contact Song? Could we now get going on our journey together?

It took several sessions and much experimentation before I became sharply aware of the possibilities that this song held for Darryl. Of course! Use of the "pop" in the song could serve a very definite purpose—it could be used to mobilize his untapped energy, to activate his physical power. As I sang the song, I held his hand and we moved around a circle that I had chalked on the floor. Darryl dragged his feet listlessly, mouthing a word here and there with what (with a stretch of imagination), might be described as enthusiasm. The tempo and volume were moderate until the "pop!" At that moment inspiration struck like lightning. I increased the volume of my voice and quickened the movement of my arms as I sought out both his hands, popping mine against his with a loud "pop!" His eyes flashed—you might say "popped"— toward my eyes, making direct contact with me for the first time. Then a fleeting smile. A spark of liveliness flickered over his face. His hands and arms flowed with a spurt of energy. His hands had met mine with an impact that we both felt. We were together, sharing something new—coexperiencing, coexisting. Yes, we had found Our Contact Song.

After that, we went around the cobbler's bench many times in many ways singing and moving to:

> All around the cobbler's bench,
> The monkey chased the weasel,
> The monkey thought t'was all in fun,
> Pop! goes the weasel.

Gradually, Darryl sang the song with me, more and more clearly enunciating the words (with the exception of pronouncing "around" as "awound" which didn't bother either of us) and with

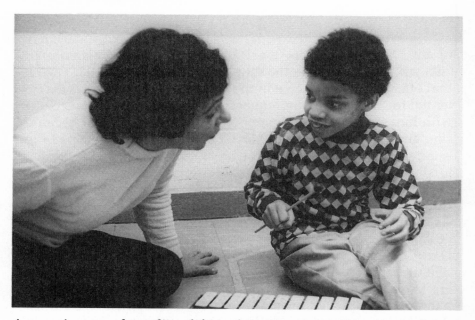

increasing tonal quality, lifting his arms in anticipation of the "pop!" At times, this song took on the nature of a private joke between us. When we would meet in the corridors, or at the lunchroom, or in his classroom, we would sing the song to each other and "pop" our hands at each other. Although I used a variety of music with him, it was this song that opened up the beginnings of a very definite line of communication between us that would need tender nurturing.

Diverse musical instruments were used in the course of treatment: drums, Latin percussion instruments such as maracas and claves, the xylophone, and an autoharp. (The small room that had become my music therapy room had no piano. I soon realized that it was an advantage inasmuch as it is imperative to be as physically accessible to the autistic child as possible.) At the session after discovering Our Contact Song, Darryl, on his own initiative, sought out the xylophone and reached for a mallet. I sat by, watching, listening. Was I hearing "Pop! Goes the Weasel"? Yes. I witnessed a completely focused Darryl leaning over the instrument, his head bent in deep concentration, singing the words of the song, intent upon reproducing the sounds of the melody on the xylophone:

Alll —— a–wound —— the —— cobb—leers —— bench ——,

The — mon—key — chased ——— the—weasel ——,

The — mon——key —— thought — t'was all in —— fun ——,

Pop! ——— goes ——— the—weasel.

And again and again until the melody sounded the way he heard it in his head. He worked at it diligently. After several attempts, his playing began to flow more rhythmically, phrase by phrase. How determined he was, especially when he encountered the difficult interval of a major 6th from the word "fun" to "pop!" With intense concentration, he went back to the beginning of a phrase, repeated the melodic line until he played it to his own satisfaction. His power of organization was truly a wonder to behold. The structure of the music was an integrating force. By the end of the next half hour, he had played the song through in the key of G major, each time more easily finding the "pop!"— articulating it with a vigor that marked a noticeable change in his energy level.

At the next session, he not only played the song through accurately, *he transposed the entire song into the key of F major.* In this key, it was the B flat on the word "the" after "goes" that presented a challenge. After a series of trials and errors, always guided by the sounds of his own singing, *he got it.* And *he* knew it. He seemed to find the tonality of this key more gratifying—a better match for his voice. This apparent awareness held great promise. Darryl's sense of self was growing. With a profound feeling for what this extraordinary achievement could mean for Darryl's development, I gave him the best acknowledgment I could think of—I hugged him.

I witnessed a totally different being from the elusive, fragmented one I had worked with, observed, experienced until then. He had internalized this music, had brought it to conscious expression—not parroting another but as one in tune with a purposefully acting Self.

However, the roller coaster that a severely disturbed person rides is steep and has dangerous curves. The course of therapy is never a straight and narrow path and the journey with Darryl was unpredictable, to say the least. There is progress, there are setbacks, forward movement and retreats—all requiring sensitive handling. He was showing encouraging signs of integration and stability: exhibiting the ability to participate in a variety of musical activities, physically asserting himself with more energy, expressing feelings gesturally (several times he put his arm around my neck and touched my face lovingly with his hand), and very willingly—yes, happily—entering into musical games with another child whom I arranged to have at several sessions as an experiment for encouraging contact with his peers.

Life with and for Darryl would then go along comparatively smoothly. In addition to music therapy sessions, we would eat lunch together or take a walk along the river or I would put aside time to watch him in the playground (where he always played alone) or go to the school office to find a typewriter for him to use. As with playing the xylophone, I discovered that he loved typing. He would go down the paper spelling out such things as the sentence: *Weasel   goes   the   pop*, in that order, and an announcement he must have heard on the radio, "stand by for *eye*dentification," with phonetic spelling. We enjoyed these moments thoroughly. Our relationship was growing deeper and was well-known to the rest of the staff, including the director, social worker, and, of course, his teacher.

Darryl's stability was fragile. Although there were episodes during which he would regress and seemingly lose hold of the gains he had made, he would regain his equilibrium through becoming engaged in a variety of music activities: playing instruments on which he could not only vent his churned-up emotions but derive pleasure. While I sang folk songs, we strummed the autoharp together, and he would hum and sing a word here and there. We would do action songs and body movements around the room together. I recorded what he was doing, what we were doing together, and the sound of his voice, playing them back to enhance his *awareness of self and another*. He would listen to his own voice with a look that could only be described as rapture while I chanted, "That is you—Darryl—playing the drum or strumming the autoharp. And I—Edi—am playing and singing with you." Darryl was integrating a state of more relatedness, awareness, and responsiveness.

And then came an SOS from his teacher. One Monday morning after spending a weekend at home, Darryl arrived on the school bus crying uncontrollably. He was in trouble. Luckily I was free to rush to his classroom. I had witnessed him in agonized states several times before. However, he would become stabilized rather quickly, going through a ritual of touching a specific spot on the wall, then a bench, then attempting to play the song he had played flawlessly the session before, and finally coming to me for comfort as I sat and sang his special song over and over and over. After several repetitions of this ritual, each time getting to play more of the melody, he successfully played through the song, reaching a measure of integration and calm that he happily sustained for extended periods of time. But he was again in trouble.

When I entered the otherwise empty classroom, I heard sounds that were coming from the deepest caverns in him—sounds that were utterly heartrending, his face distorted, his glazed eyes unseeing.

"Thank goodness you're here," exclaimed the distraught teacher. "I've tried everything—EVERYTHING—and nothing has worked. He's been this way all morning. I don't know what happened at home. He's been upset before by the change from going home for a weekend and then coming back here, but I've never seen him this disturbed. And I know how he's been responding to music therapy. To put it mildly, we're really lucky that you're here this morning."

Nor had I ever seen him in such extreme torment but I knew instinctively what Darryl needed. Without a second of hesitation, I crawled under the desk and softly hummed the song that had become Our Contact Song. Had the director walked in at that moment, she would have come upon a most unusual sight—a music therapist crouching under a small desk, offering a xylophone to an extremely agitated Darryl.

The very Friday before, Darryl had played his special song in both the keys of G and F major. Now, his every attempt failed. He was in such a frantic state that the progress he had made had dissipated into thin air. To nurture this sensitive young person who so loved to play the xylophone and who had come to feel safe with me, to help him be relieved of his anguish, to bring some measure of harmony and balance to his troubled soul, to assist him to recover the integration he had achieved—that was the music therapist/ human being I felt called upon to be.

It seemed like an eternity before Darryl showed any sign of being able to move out of the shattered state he was in. I sang Our Contact Song. I hummed the melody, I played it on his favorite instrument I stroked his head tenderly. I sang his name in muted tones. I sang my name gently to let him know that I was there with him. "Darryl, I'm here with you. Edi is here with you." I was silent. I touched his tightly-clenched hand. As I did so, the relentless wailing lessened, his fingers stirred under my cautious touch, his lowered head slowly lifted. Darryl was coming back.

I was on the alert for any sign of his "return." I didn't think about time. I would stay with him as long as he needed my caring support. I knew that once he was able to play his special song, his highly vulnerable organism stood a chance of recovering from this devastating episode. The essence of the music therapy process is to tap and develop and nurture the wellness that exists in the human being. I would make available every assistance possible to contact the healthy Darryl through music.

The wonder of it all was that Darryl's "organic music" had surfaced months before. Now, we could draw upon the power of his music—his music making—to heal the recently inflicted wound. With delicate care, I nourished the healthy self. Under his desk, we worked together at melding the bits and pieces of Our Contact Song into a melodious, rhythmic, harmonious whole. Through it, Darryl became whole.

It was not long after that Darryl and I went for a walk out-doors—a walk that may have been a milestone in his life. After sauntering along, enjoying the warmth of a May sun, we sat down on a cement block. Suddenly, Darryl tugged at my arm and virtu-ally commanded, in a loud resonant voice, "Get up! Get up!" *This was his first self-initiated verbal communication to me.* I not only an-swered immediately, "Yes, Darryl, I'll get up," I stood up—in fact, bolted up—my heart skipping a beat. Darryl had taken the leap that is rarely achieved by the autistic child—intentional verbal ex-pression. We were sharing what is referred to in humanistic psy-chology as a "peak experience." Acknowledging him verbally and gesturally, we fairly skipped back to the school, hand in hand.

A week later, going from his classroom to the music ther-apy room, we walked past a candy vending machine in the corri-dor of the school. Again, Darryl tugged at my arm. Encouraging him to speak, I answered his signal. "Yes, Darryl, what do you want?" Turning his head to me, he declared, as if speaking asser-tively were the most natural thing in the world, "I want Snicker."

Was that Darryl saying "I"? Leaning toward him, our eyes met. His were wide with excitement as he repeated even more as-sertively, *"I want Snicker—pleezzzz."*

KATHY: NN NN NN NN NN —"SEE HOW I'M JUMPING"

Again and again, I wonder about the knowing that goes beyond consciously learning and training and applying skills and techniques. And I ask, "What is intuition?" For me, I have come to see intuition as a flash of awareness that surfaces from the recesses of the prepared mind. What I came to call Our Contact Song in the context of *A Continuum of Awareness* originated in that way.

I approached the director of recreation at Manhattan Developmental Center, Ellen Ashton, to volunteer my services as music therapist at that state residential facility. After my giving a description and explanation of the nature of this treatment modality, she was most receptive to the idea. Immediately, she thought it would be of benefit to one child in particular who was in dire need of individualized treatment. That child was seven and a half year old lonely Kathy.

When Kathy was brought into the music therapy room for her first session, I saw a lovely child walk stiff-leggedly on tiptoe to the chair I extended to her. She sat down, clutching a Ping-Pong ball with both hands, her shoulders hunched, her far-away green eyes gazing into space. Seating myself in a chair opposite her, I leaned forward as I sang, "Hello, Kathy—hello, Kathy. I'm so glad to see you. Hello, Kathy—I'm *so glad* to see you." My greeting song floated away from her and evaporated. From her lack of response, it dawned on me that "hello," even when sung, probably sounded like any other word she might hear. Actually, did she hear it at all? Or, if she did hear it, did it mean anything to her? There was no sign that it did. In fact, I quickly realized that it was as if I didn't exist for her. Until there was some kind of connection between us, *no thing*, *nothing* would bring us together. I wouldn't be able to make contact with her. Kathy was in her own world, seemingly oblivious of me. Kathy was diagnosed as autistic.

This is the saga of how a Ping-Pong ball played an all-important role in making the first contact with Kathy. At the second session, she came in clutching the same ball, but this time ran and jumped around the room, throwing it hither and yon. I literally shadowed her, observing her every move; her actions appeared to be random, impulsive, and joyless. She paid no attention to my singing her name and my name and what she was doing. This went on for at least five minutes and then, from a repertoire of songs that were stored in my memory bank, and, I believe,

in my psyche, the Flemish Folk Song, "See How I'm Jumping," surfaced. I spontaneously sang and adapted words to the tune:

Kathy is bouncing, bouncing, bouncing,
Kathy is bouncing like a ball,
Kathy is bouncing, bouncing, bouncing,
Kathy is bouncing like a ball.
She didn't know she could bounce so high,
She didn't know that she could stand————— still,
Kathy is jumping, jumping, jumping,
When she gets tired, down———— she———— falls . . .

Kathy's response was astounding. She listened, seemingly aware of what the words meant. However, it would take many more sessions before the true meaning and significance of what I called Our Contact Song would come to light. The concept behind the contact song is that it evokes the very first *reciprocal* communication initiated by the client to the therapist. Essentially, it is the first two-way communication through music that opens the lines of communication on all possible levels ranging from gestural to speech.

The realization of the contact song as a stimulator of reciprocal communication came sooner than I had hoped for with

Kathy. At the fourth session, after bouncing around the room to-gether and throwing and catching the Ping-Pong ball while I sang "See How I'm Jumping," improvising words to suit whatever we were doing, using the strategies *Reflection* and *Identification*. Kathy lay down on the floor and lapsed into wiggling her fingers close to her face. I was practically lying on top of her, singing:

> Kathy is wiggling, wiggling her fingers,
> Kathy is wiggling her fingers now.

As I started to sing the next phrase, Kathy stopped the mannerism that had become so familiar. She *looked directly up at me* and sang the song, in the exact tempo, the exact rhythmic pat-terns, the exact tonality:

> Nn NnNn Nn Nn
> Nn Nn Nn Nn
> Nn NnNn Nn Nn
> Nn Nn Nnnnnnn.

In the middle of a word I was singing, completely taken by sur-prise, I instantaneously switched gears and sang back,

> Kathy is singing, singing, singing,
> Kathy is singing Nn Nn Nn,
> Kathy is singing, singing, singing,
> Kathy is singing Nn Nn Nn.

You work for a breakthrough, a shift in awareness—searching, wondering how and when it will come about. And here it was. Kathy had initiated a communication to me through music that proved to be the foundation for a deep and long-lasting rela-tionship.

Dr. Kenneth Bruscia, then director of the New York Uni-versity Music Therapy Program and a key professor in my music therapy training at New York University, was observing the ses-sion. After Kathy left, we discussed Kathy's breakthrough, a once-in-a-lifetime happening that had far-reaching implications. Kathy and I had made the contact that was critical for establishing a therapeutic relationship—a human relationship. We could now work together.

Dr. Bruscia and I both expressed our excitement. How fortuitous that he had witnessed the kind of "momentous" event that we look for in the music therapy process. One of his comments was especially enlightening for it gave insight into an aspect of Kathy that would be important to explore: It looked as if Kathy was telling me, with a touch of defiance, "You're not the only one who can sing, I can sing too!"

Aha! Was this a clarion call for the connection I had been seeking? *Something* had occurred. "Yes, Kathy, yes Kathy. You can sing too! Let us sing to each other. I think we'll get to know each other in that way—to share—maybe even to have fun together. Let me get to know you —anything and everything about you. And that *is* what happened. Through song, a close bond evolved. Our relationship grew in leaps and bounds. Music therapy wove its magic and I became more and more aware, from my experience of and with Kathy, of how it could work miracles through music therapy.

In the perceptive book about her autistic daughter, *The Siege: The First Eight Years of an Autistic Child*, Clara Claiborne Parks talks about "as ifs." In light of that, the music therapist needs to be aware that many things *seem to be* or *are apparently so.* My writings, particularly about autistic children, are peppered with "as ifs." Through Kathy I discovered that many things I thought were not there or not possible, may be there or are possible—namely that the autistic child may be *actively experiencing* in an entirely unique way, may look *as if* oblivious of other human beings and what is going on. *I knew that Kathy held a key to my Tao as a music therapist.* What and how to make a relationship with one who appeared to be living on a different plane from mine, whose behavior was bewildering, unpredictable, unfathomable, as if out-of-touch with the external environment and shut off from other human beings. I felt strongly that I would reach her organic being through music. That it would bring us together on a mutually revelatory journey.

Bouncing and running everywhere and anywhere after the ping-pong ball, no matter where she threw it, Kathy caught it with unfailing accuracy, speedily repeating the movement around and around the spacious music therapy room. Not a ripple of her tightly-held muscles, not a flicker of her fixed eyelids, not a lowering of her aloofly-held head. Nothing existed for Kathy but the Ping-Pong ball. Or so it seemed.

In the next weeks, whenever Kathy was brought for her hour-long one-to-one sessions, her constant "companion" was the little ball. She would clutch it to her and run hyperactively around the room. Then, suddenly resorting to self-stimulation, she would often lapse into stiff-legged rocking, her body moving diagonally, her shoulders hunched, her eyes looking inward. I spent these sessions being there fully for "lonely" Kathy whose life I was sharing—feeling compassion for this young human being, exploring the possibility of reaching her. When, how would I contact her and help bring her out of her isolation? How could I penetrate the autistic barrier that was keeping her locked in her own world, that was preventing her from having a loving mother-daughter relationship, that was depriving her of experiencing the joy and fun and pain of being a child?

I chose to play the autoharp—a musical instrument that would not separate me from her (as would a piano)—and sang songs I thought might evoke a response, wondering when she would show a sign of being aware of herself, of being aware of me. Having had the experience of working with Darryl, I anticipated, with a mixture of emotions, the challenging process of experimentation, exploration, discovery, and frustration that work with an autistic child entails. (Interestingly enough, one of the principles of the modern Gestalt school of psychology and psychotherapy—upon which much of my work is based—is that frustration can be a positive force, stimulating creative solutions to a challenge or problem.)

The common denominator of early childhood autism is the autistic barrier that interferes with accepted norms of functioning. From my studies and research, I learned of the many clusters of symptoms that it can present and that, just as with all human beings, there are no two children with this condition who are alike. Darryl's cluster of autistic symptoms were different from Kathy's. For one thing, he had an echolalic speech pattern: when I sang, "I am Edi, you are Darryl" he sang back, "I am Edi, you are Darryl. Kathy had no speech. She had *one special sound—Nn, Nn, Nn—that would burst forth, mostly at moments when she appeared to be agitated or frustrated.* Maybe one day when I sang, "Hi, Kathy," she would sing back to me "Nn, Nn Nn." as if saying "Hi, Edi."

The moment she would get caught up in rocking—a prevalent autistic behavior—I would take her hands in mine and rock back and forth with her, "singing into" the rhythmic movements. In this music therapy adaptation of the psychotherapist Carl Rogers' technique, *Reflection*, there is instantaneous musical playback of the here-and-now child. Reflection through song and

movement may be the child's only thread of "reality." So, as with Kathy, if the child has a mannerism such as finger wiggling, I would wiggle my fingers too and transform it into a musical experience, singing and/or chanting about it. If it is compulsive rocking, I would rock with her and swing it into a steady beat. If it is idiosyncratic vocalizing, I vocalized too, reflecting her sound, weaving it into a melody. As the inspiring New Zealand teacher Sylvia Ashton-Warner so humanly expresses it, "I reach a hand into the mind of the child, bring out a handful of the stuff I find there, and use that as our first working material. Whether it is good or bad stuff, coloured or dun . . . the stuff of the child . . . whatever and wherever the child" (1964, pp. 31 & 32).

It was the "stuff" of Kathy that I used to awaken, expand, and heighten her awareness of herself and of me. This approach to treatment is based in the humanistic school of psychology and psychotherapy, an approach which differs in a fundamental way from a behaviorist approach: On the wall of the "autistic unit" at Manhattan Developmental Services where Kathy lived on a respite basis for several months away from her home, the behaviorist psychologist had posted a list of her behaviors and so-called bizarre mannerisms that *should be eliminated.* Behavioral change is quantified through external, mechanistic means of rewards for repeating an action x-number of times—as you may have seen trainers of dolphins at SeaWorld do—or stopping an undesirable action. With a view to achieving *qualitative* change, I did just the opposite! My approach, giving the child to herself, is designed to have the person internalize changes. In humanistic terms, this means intrinsic learning, transformation of the person's perceptions and feelings and actions. I use symptoms, behaviors, and mannerisms to establish a relationship—to let the child know that another, a caring person, accepts and acknowledges her for who she is. Once that connection is made, the aim is to transform the symptoms into behaviors and actions that nurture and nourish the child.

Our Contact Song went through many variations on a theme that reflected and identified what Kathy was doing, what I was doing, what we were doing together: Using it in myriad ways provided security while the varied activities and identifying words counteracted perseveration and the need for sameness:

> Kathy is rocking, rocking, rocking,
> Kathy is rocking back and forth

> Kathy and Edi are rocking, rocking,
> Kathy and Edi are rocking back and forth.

And more and more. . .

> Kathy is smiling—singing—jumping—
> beating the drum . . .
> Kathy is wiggling her fingers—bouncing her ball—sitting
> on Edi's lap . . .
> Kathy is clapping her hands to the music . . .
> Kathy and Edi are playing a game . . .
> Edi is tickling Kathy's knees and Kathy is laughing . . .

Bringing the child to conscious levels of experiencing herself and others is a process of flux and influx, steps forward and backward, peak experiences and setbacks. As Juliette Alvin says, "a musical experience can satisfy the child's need for non-verbal self-expression" (1978, p. 3) and I was constantly on the alert to provide musical experiences that would go with the flow of Kathy's mercurial moods. For example, as she would become hyperkinetic or hyperactive or start to hyperventilate (breath hard), these were cues for a complete contrast in mood and quality of the music and the activity. (Hyperactivity, however, is not to be confused with healthy release of emotional and physical tension, although the thread between the two is often thin, demanding cautious and flexible guidance.)

There is much in the process of finding the expressive self of the autistic child through music. Kathy came to me very early in my personal exploration and application of the art and science of music therapy. The insight that she came into my life for a purpose has an overwhelming impact on me. For it was through seeking ways to meet the needs of this lovely, lonely child that I sought and found a most telling context for my approach to the practice of music therapy, *A Continuum of Awareness*, (see the earlier chapter in this volume) which has been recognized as a pioneering contribution to the profession.

A number of years after creating this context, I was struck by an inspiring passage in Abraham Maslow's book, *The Farther Reaches of Human Nature* (1974). In his fully-human, discerning view, "The pioneer, the creator, the explorer . . . has to be a courageous man, not afraid to stick his neck out, not afraid even to make mistakes . . . that he comes to tentative conclusions in the absence of facts and then spends some years trying to find out if his hunch was correct." I felt completely attuned—in sync—with this great, innovative thinker (despite the use of the masculine gender!). What an affirmation it was for me!

Yes, there are peak experiences, plateaus, frustrations, chaos to order, order to chaos, moments of anguish, bursts of joy. Sustained by a positive attitude throughout trials and errors and "successes," together Kathy and I courageously forged the way to the expressive Self that lay behind what seemed at times an impenetrable barrier.

A month and a half after I had begun to see Kathy, her extremely attractive and highly articulate mother sought me out at the Christmas party held at the Center, animatedly exclaiming, "*You're* the music therapist! I'm so happy to meet you. I can't begin to tell you what a change there's been in Kathy since the last time she came to spend time at home. She's a changed child. She's been singing *all the time.*, she seems to like one tune best." I smiled knowingly, fully intending to go into this with her, but not wanting to interrupt the enthusiastic flow. "She's even been laughing—something she's never done before. And affectionate! I can hardly believe she's the same child. She's been sitting on my lap and letting me put my arms around her. All the way here in the taxi, she was singing her one special syllable. I guess you know the one I mean. I can't thank you enough. I really never thought the day would come when Kathy would be—so happy. . . ."

I put my arm around Kathy as we sang Our Contact Song to each other. This was a big moment for all three of us.

Later that afternoon, I was able to spend time with Kathy's mother. I went into detail about the nature of the music therapy process with Kathy and suggested that she, as the parent, could enter into the process—that it would undoubtedly be very beneficial for both of them. She was more than willing—she was intensely moved at the prospect of being involved with her newly-found daughter. I arranged to visit Kathy at her home as well as to have sessions at my home. Kathy not only took these changes in her stride, she was having fun.

Although Kathy was transferred to another special education setting, I maintained contact with her and her mother. Eight years after leaving MDC, they returned to pay me a visit. She had acquired a few words which she used with gestures to communicate with me. And she still remembered our song which we sang together nostalgically but joyously. Now, these many years later, she is living in a group home with four other young people, and, as her mother proudly describes her, being "a regular teenager," going to dances and parties and attending a special workshop.

What warms my heart and brings tears of joy to my eyes is her mother telling me, with tears of joy in *her* eyes, "Kathy wouldn't be the person she is today if it hadn't been for you and music therapy."

MARGARITA: I WANT PI—AHN—NOH

Music therapy was gaining the attention of the staff. Many were seeing the possibilities for the various clients and asked to have me work with them. I would often visit the "apartments" (as the living quarters of the clients were called) to arrange either individual or group sessions. A psychologist had referred Margarita.

When I sought her out, she was standing in a ramrod position close to a wall, her deep cherry-black eyes staring vacantly into space. Silently, I watched her urgently wrapping and unwrapping, wrapping and unwrapping a leather belt around her left arm and hand. Her intensity and manual skill were astounding—qualities that I got to know well and would see transformed into amazing musical expressiveness. She didn't notice me at all. At least, I don't think she did. Startlingly beautiful, thirteen year-old Margarita is a prime example of one whose unawareness of self and others was all-pervasive, whose energies were caught up in compulsive and self-abusive behaviors. No communicative language had ever developed.

While waiting for a propitious moment to approach her, a stream of utterances, unintelligible but with a distinct Spanish flavor, gushed forth, interspersed with high-toned sounds emitted in a bird-like fashion from her extended neck. If only she could tell me what she was experiencing! Had she ever seen or heard this in her early childhood when she lived at home? I could only wonder and hope that I would get to know the Margarita who was trapped inside. I touched her elbow cautiously and in a straightforward manner said, "Margarita, you and I—we are going to my room. Do you understand what I'm saying? We are going to my room." Still wrapping the leather belt around her arm, *not missing a beat*, she allowed me to lead her to the music therapy room. Once there, she sat on a chair immobile except for the same perseverative, repetitious belt wrapping. Then a yawn with one hand to her ear in a characteristically self-stimulatory gesture. We were two people in close physical proximity but separated by a opaque veil of unawareness.

From these tenuous beginnings, however, not only did a trusting relationship develop but the talent that had lain dormant and untapped, emerged, to the amazement of everyone who knew her. Becoming aware of the fear and distrust that stemmed from the physical and emotional abuse she had suffered, the work with

Margarita necessitated every possible means of establishing *basic trust*, a key psychotherapeutic principle of the notable humanitarian, Erik Erikson.

Several weekly sessions were spent on "getting acquainted time"—"getting to *trust* time." Vocally and instrumentally, I reflected her idiosyncratic (uniquely personal) outpourings. I wrapped and unwrapped with her the ever-present leather belt as I sang the spiritual, "There's a Little Wheel A 'Turnin' in My Heart," with words and rhythmic flow adapted to her preoccupation with the belt. In essence I was sending her a message: I am with you, I see you, I hear you, I am joining you in your world. Maybe you will see me, hear me, be with me, join me in this outside world. Together, let's find healthy outlets for your pent-up creative energy. As with all autistic persons, the need to establish rapport is a prerequisite for treatment. Without contact, there is experiencing on unaware levels but not on the aware levels of *co*-experiencing or *inter*experiencing upon which a trusting relationship is built.

The safety of being one-to-one with someone who played music for her and sang songs to her and let her choose all sorts of musical instruments to play was certainly new to her. Now, when I came to take her to a session, she would grasp my hand and practically pull me toward my room. Her determination was nothing short of phenomenal when there was something she wanted.

As we moved closer to each other, Margarita's needs and wants began to become more evident. Not having language available, she expressed herself in rather explosive ways, most often with what is referred to as a *lack of impulse control*. When the impulse to play the triangle, for instance, came over her, she just grabbed it. When she didn't want to play a tambourine that I might offer her, she would simply push it away. At one session, as I freely strummed the autoharp, creating different musical effects—loud and soft, slow and fast, high and low—in a flash Margarita snatched the autoharp from me (still holding onto her leather belt) and ran her fingers over the strings, lowering her left ear to hear and feel the vibrations. As she strummed, she dropped the leather belt and laughed with delight—the very first show of this facet of her personality. It was as if she was enjoying a joke! I enjoyed the joke too. This was the opening for many such moments we were to share: for deeply-felt experiences, for the gamut of emotions, for the trusting relationship that developed and was put to the acid test at a time when Margarita had an hysterical attack of fear.

The night that the entire building had to be evacuated because of a gas leak, all staff members were drafted to help. We were transferred to another facility. The other clients had settled in and had gone to sleep. But not Margarita. She was panic-stricken by the change. I was called to stay with her. I sat with her for hours, softly singing and humming songs she was familiar with—particularly Our Contact Song—until she was calm enough to go to sleep.

As sessions went along, although I offered her other instruments—a drum or xylophone—she pushed them aside, choosing to engulf herself in the sea of sounds and vibrations that her very own fingers produced. The autoharp took on a major role in establishing a trusting relationship with her. We had fun exploring different kinds of sound effects, I playing chords by depressing the chord bars while she strummed. We were making music together. And then I wondered, "What song or music would appeal to her?" So far, there was only lukewarm response to the various songs I had used for music-movement activities. What might get a rise out of her? What might have a familiar ring? Being of Hispanic heritage, maybe "La Cucaracha." To the melody and rhythm of that song, I improvised the words:

> Margarita, Margarita,
> Margarita is *your* name,
> Margarita, Margarita,
> Margarita is *your* name.

and

> Edi, Edi,
> Edi is *my* name,
> Edi, Edi,
> Edi is *my* name.

> Margarita, Margarita.
> Margarita is playing the harp.
> Margarita, Margarita,
> Margarita is playing the harp.

and

Margarita and Edi,

Are playing the harp,

Margarita and Edi,

Are playing the harp.

Some weeks later, Margarita and I were sitting together on a piano bench while I played the song on the piano, singing:

Margarita, Margarita,
Margarita is your name.

Suddenly, in her impulsive way and with intense energy, she pushed me to the edge of the bench (almost off it) and positioned herself plunk in the middle. What I heard was truly miraculous. Margarita was playing clusters of the chords I had been playing to accompany the melody of what was now—for us—"Margarita's Song." With her left hand she played the chordal sequence—the I (tonic) chord for the first phrase, changed to the IV (subdominant) chord for the second phrase, then to the V (dominant) chord for the third phrase, and then back to the I (tonic) chord for the fourth phrase—all in the rhythmic patterns of the song with a steady pulse that brought a gasp from my throat. I rushed to sit next to her on the piano bench. My emotions were running high, my voice vibrating with joy: "Margarita, that was fantastic. Let's play it together." I didn't have to urge her. She went right into the chordal structure again. I played the melody. We were sharing an extraordinary musical experience—an extraordinary human experience. We were *in contact* with each other. She turned to me with a look of trust in her beautiful eyes.

In succeeding sessions she couldn't wait to get her hands on the piano. We would hardly be inside the door of the music therapy room when she would rush to the piano to attempt to play music that she might of heard, for example, on the radio. One such effort was a garbled but recognizable version of Chopin's "Minute Waltz." Then she came up with a chordal sequence: E dominant 7th, A minor, E dominant 7th, A minor, B minor, A minor, E dominant 7th, A minor, and a rhythmic pattern that immediately suggested a prototypical Russian melody to me. Margarita's left hand literally *flew* over the keyboard, her fingers landing in astoundingly accurate "formation." I kept pace with her, playing "The Russian Melody" in every minor key, including unthinkable ones such as F-sharp minor and D-flat minor.

What the unfoldment of Margarita's gift for the piano—what the *unleashing* of her passion for the piano—led to went beyond the joy and sense of self that Margarita gained from playing the piano. It was a path to the overall goal of music therapy—to effect a transfer of abilities to the person's daily living, to help fulfill the potential to function on as fully human a level as possible. Specifically for Margarita, awareness of herself, her relations to others, and to the environment could be transformed by means of the ability to communicate through verbal language.

Until treatment through music therapy, there seems to have been an acceptance that she was not capable of intelligible speech. But, although the critical developmental period of acquiring speech had passed, I firmly believed that there was a chance that Margarita would be able to use words and word phrases that had meaning for her. She certainly had innate intelligence. What had been missing was the caring help and intervention that would tap her creative being—that could provide her with alternatives to the unbridled manner of functioning that had become habitual. She was ready for change. The discovery that music was a natural means of expressivity for her opened up the possibility. *And all important, she trusted me.*

The approach I used with her clearly exemplifies the conscious application of the science and the art of music therapy. I explored and experimented with and spent many hours of thought about how to meet the challenge that Margarita presented. I brought to bear the music therapy methods and techniques that could be used for her particular needs. I called upon my intuitive, my instinctive, my total creative self to guide me.

Setting out on a continuum of awareness, we worked on isolated words of a song that she especially liked—"Over the Rainbow"—concentrating on words that had rhyming sounds such as "high" and "sky." Margarita was very responsive. She began to enjoy this new game. Singing isolated words of a song grew into improvising songs that specifically dealt with her impulsivity. If she got the urge to play a record, she just ran to the record player. If she wanted to play the triangle, she dashed to the instrument board. If she wanted a cookie (I kept cookies in a drawer for a social time with her after sessions), she was into the cabinet before I could blink an eye. Complaints about this kind of behavior came from all sources. However, sadly enough, restraints were the usual way of coping.

At every session, I worked with her to express her wants and needs through words rather than impulsive actions. At first, when she wanted something such as a record, I would ask, "Margarita, what do you want? Do you want record?" Holding the record out to her, I would repeat, "Want record?" Then, I began to anticipate her impulses. Handing her a record, I would ask, "Margarita, do you want record? *Want record?*" Giving her an instrument she liked such as the triangle, I ask, "Margarita, do you want the triangle? *Want triangle?*" Giving a cookie to her, would be, "Margarita do you want a cookie? *Want cookie?*"

Very soon she showed signs of becoming aware that my repeating the words, "Want _____?" were a cue for her to say them also. She was paying attention to what I was saying and doing. She was making the connection between wanting something, and the actual object or the action she would take. With this development came her first aware verbal communication. Margarita began to say, "Want _____."

The next stage was adding "I" at the beginning of the verbal phrases she was learning to use. We had succeeded in achieving the goal of using words, but to come to the point where she would say "I want" with a sense of her own identity would be a quantum leap. Of course, we already know that Margarita's passion for the piano was her uppermost *want*. She'd push me aside as I was opening the door to the music therapy room, and dash with utter unawareness of anything but wanting to get to the piano. Since I couldn't hand the piano to her, I would sit beside her, saying, "Yes, Margarita, you want to play the piano." Perhaps the intense desire would awaken her awareness of being the "I" who so wanted the piano.

The process of verbalizing "*I* want" took hold through the meaning that the piano had for her—through her intense desire for this "object" through which she made the music inside her come to life. Before entering the music therapy room with her, I would ask, "Do you want to play the piano? Can you say, '*I* want piano.' " After many trials and repetitions, she told me in no uncertain terms, "*I want pi —ahn ——-noh.*"

RICKI'S FIRST WORDS: DAY BY DAY

Ricki, a resident of a State facility for developmentally disabled persons, was in a music therapy group with Lloyd, Santa, and Angel—all in the 20—30 year chronological age range. Their functioning was in the severe mental retardation category. All four had no speech. Sessions were really heartwarming. Except for Lloyd's mannerism of rubbing his hands together constantly and falling asleep while doing so or even when he smilingly seemed to be present to the music therapy process—except for these "bizarre" behaviors, the sessions flowed along like a peaceful river. Angel—slow-moving, silent Angel—never made waves. In fact, it was usually necessary to arouse him to attend. His eyes looked as if he was focusing them on me or on an instrument, but his capacity to grasp what was going on was extremely limited. When I would sing out his name and take his hands in mine to stimulate the sensation of clapping them together, of hearing the sound that his hands made as they clapped, or help him have the kinesthetic experience of using a drumstick to beat a drum to the music, he would smile benignly and gaze into my eyes with a look that his name aptly describes—angelic. And Santa, peaceful Santa, sat virtually still, immobile except for her legs which would swing back and forth, back and forth, most often out of sync with the pulse of the music. She wavered from being fearful to lowering her head in a gesture of withdrawal. On the whole, Ricki wore a look of blissful equanimity. Yet, there were moments when she displayed uncontrollable anger—or was it frustration? There were many group and individual goals. To awaken their awareness of themselves and each other, I sang their names throughout the sessions. If Ricki lifted her hand, I would acknowledge her immediately by singing, "Ricki is moving her arm—*up—p——pppp.*"

At that time, one of the songs that I enjoyed singing and playing was "Day by Day" from the musical *Jesus Christ Superstar.* I had been searching and exploring various songs, particularly folk songs that have repetitious lyrics, for the purpose of stimulating verbalization. At a session, well into the course of therapy with this group, I went through the process of following my intuition as well as the conscious awareness that this song had the very features needed for working on speech development and improvement (an all-important goal for developmentally disabled people). The words "day by day" are ever-present, rhyming words such as "clearly," "dearly," "nearly" can be effective in evoking phonation particularly when enunciation is exaggerated by the therapist (a music therapy technique that I used frequently with exceptional results), and I had created a piano arrangement of the song that I very much enjoyed playing. Certainly the elements were conducive to the work at hand.

Always on the alert for any signs of not only response but arousal that can activate a person on different organismic levels—physical, psychological, mental, psychosocial—I saw that each member of the group was having an active response to the music: Lloyd grinned broadly and rubbed his hands together with delight, Santa's legs were moving back and forth, Angel's face broke into a beatific smile. But it was Ricki who was going through what seemed to be a transformation—a shift in perception, a main principle of my work that I derived from modern Gestalt therapy. As never before, her body began to sway in perfect harmony with the pulse of the music: head thrust forward, eyes riveted on me, face alive with rapt focus, lips forming the words "day by day."

"Ricki, Ricki, you are singing 'day——by——day.' Lloyd, Santa, Angel—Ricki is *singing* 'day——by——day.' Isn't it wonderful!" I exclaimed, noting to myself that this was not just a great *moment* for Ricki. The deeper implication was that a *shift in awareness* had taken place—the kind of shift that my approach to the music therapy process, *A Continuum of Awareness*, is designed to effect. What is more, the other three in the group understood that something special had happened to Ricki and acknowledged her in their own way—pointing and smiling. For the first time in her life, this shy flower was showered with attention and appreciation. No doubt about it, Ricki was blooming.

One of the remarkable benefits of music therapy is speech development. In the group process, the therapist formulates goals and objectives for the group and for each individual. A music therapy assessment of each person precedes treatment. As for Ricki, the assessment indicated potential for speech, but there had been no movement according to the speech therapist. A technique that serves many therapeutic purposes and is especially useful in speech development is the adaptation of words of a song to the unique needs of the person. For Ricki, I simplified the text of the song by the repetition of the three words she had tentatively voiced.

This breakthrough for Ricki filled us with excitement and joy. At sessions that followed, I incorporated the song into the therapy process in different ways. Instead of singing the text of the song as written, I sang the melodic line and rhythmic patterns in a slow tempo with exaggerated enunciation of the words:

Day   by   dayyyyy,
Day   by   dayyyyy,
Day   by   dayyyyy,
Oh, day   by   dayyyyyyy.

Day by dayyyyy,
Day by dayyyyy,
Day by dayyyyy,
Day by dayyyyy,
Day by dayyyyy,
Day   by   dayyyyyyyyyyyy.

Grasping these three words and making an effort to sing them was increasingly gratifying for Ricki and for me. With constant encouragement and nurturing at ensuing sessions, her growing awareness of her self-worth and sense of fulfillment were observable. *She*—Ricki—was consciously producing words, musical sounds. She was expressing herself in a way she had never experienced before, never had had the pleasure of doing—*she was singing*, singing with the others in the group. And we, Ricki and I, had a new relationship, one that proved to motivate growth of functioning on a higher level in areas of her daily living. She became more actively involved in special education classes, more self-sufficient in the ability to take care of her needs, and, with on-going assistance, used isolated words along with body language to communicate. The results of music therapy were confirmed by other staff members. At a case conference, there was a great deal of evidence that corroborated my report about the transformation of Ricki. I was pleased that the psychologist, who had begun to value my humanistic approach, was duly impressed!

It is inspiring to view a videotape of Ricki's valiant efforts. Seeing and hearing her voice the words "day by day" in light of her condition and history gives empirical evidence of the efficacy of using song and rhythmic patterns to stimulate speech. With Ricki, although there are limitations on her use of verbal language to communicate, what is tremendously important is that she is happier and more related to others because of the awakening and heightening of her awareness that came about through the singing of her first words—"day by day."

DONALD'S BLUES:
NO-O-O-O—I WON'T DO IT N-O-O-O-O MORE!

Donald is truly a casualty of long-term institutionalization. He was twenty-four when I first started to see him for music therapy. His condition was characterized as mild retardation. Having been institutionalized since the age of four, his developmental and functional levels suffered tragically. And despite this psychosocial deprivation and though his condition of retardation stems from mild microcephaly (small cranial size), Donald's creative talents— his verbalization, his imaginative way of expressing himself, his mechanical abilities, and his exceptional dancing skills—all are outstanding by any standards. Because he was so aware, the frustration of his life became increasingly acute. He expressed intense concern: "What is to become of my life? I want to work in a bicycle shop or dance on the stage or make a record." I, too, had such ideas about Donald—not entirely unreasonable ones were circumstances different.

For six of the thirteen years that I was at MDC, we had a very special therapeutic relationship. Because of the limitations of institutional life, Donald became more and more rebellious. However, he was ingenious. He found ways of getting around his situation, spending as much time as possible in the music therapy room with me. It became his haven. Often, while I was busy at my desk writing reports, he would ask me if he could play records or strum a guitar or dance to recordings. I observed how completely absorbed he was in what he was doing. His dancing was beautifully expressive. His grace and his timing were superb. I would watch him with mixed feelings of joy and sadness. John Travolta had nothing on Donald!

In addition to sessions of one-to-one therapy, he created a "life" for himself within the walls of the music therapy room. He would tinker with a broken record player that had been inoperable for months until he got it to work. Or he would ask to play the guitar which I would tune to one chord to give his strumming a semblance of harmonic relation to improvised songs, fancying himself as a star performer. I chose an E major 7th chord which gave his playing a blues-like quality.

Whenever I had free moments, we would sit and talk or I would take Donald to José's Restaurant around the corner for a snack. One of the goals of music therapy was to learn, through

DONALD'S BLUES

Improvisation by Donald and Edi

music, to read and spell simple words that had meaning for him. With the aim of having him learn to read by using "organic vocabulary" (in accordance with Sylvia Ashton-Warner's approach), when we went to José's Restaurant, I would help Donald read his favorite foods on the menu: "hot chocolate" and "English muffins."

Donald's impulse control was minimal. In his formative years, he was not given the guidance or opportunity to develop socialization skills. He just grew like wild grass, uncared for. Naturally intelligent and articulate, he told me much about what he had gone through at Willowbrook, a New York State institution for the developmentally disabled, where he was placed at the age of four, and that now, for the first time since being there, he felt as if someone cared about him. Deeply moved and aware of his intense desire to better himself, I wanted to be there for him as much as I possibly could. I felt that a second chance was due—overdue—for Donald. And so, our music therapy sessions, our free time together, our trips to José's Restaurant were a wellspring of possibilities for helping Donald to "become the best that he is able to become," as the humanistic psychologist, Abraham H. Maslow, so simply puts it (1976, p. 163).

One day, coming back from José's Restaurant, as we approached the entrance of MDC Donald, in his impulsive way, ran ahead of me. The door slammed in my face. Several times before, we had talked about the fact that he wasn't aware of his unintentional thoughtless behavior—that it really was something he needed to pay attention to. He would say, "Yes, Edi, I know it. I just forget. I didn't mean it." This time, I made no mention until we were inside the music therapy room. I realized that we needed to deal with this on another level as the rational approach wasn't working.

In a flash, Donald made a beeline for the guitar. "Donald," I said, " I know that you love to play the guitar. Let me tune it to your special chord—E 7th—and then how about making up a song? What do you think of the idea of singing about going to José's Restaurant and then when we got back you ran ahead of me and let the door slam in my face?" Donald 's creative juices were stimulated. He started strumming a vigorous rhythmic pattern. I supported him on the piano. We composed "Donald's Blues" together:

We went to José's Restaurant around the corner,
We went to José's Restaurant around the corner,
We went to José's Restaurant around the corner,
To get some English muffins and hot choc'late.

I love the taste of those English muffins,
 Yes, I love the taste of those English muffins,
Mmmm, I love the taste of those English muffins,
They're so delicious with hot choc'late.

When we got back from José's Restaurant,
Yes, when we got back from José's Restaurant,
When we got back from José's Restaurant,
I ran ahead and slammed the door in Edi's face.

And what do you think Edi said?
Yes, what do you think Edi said?
Mmm, what do you think Edi said?
She said, Donald, let's sit down and talk it over.

So we sat down and we talked it over,
Yes, we sat down and we talked it over,
Mm, we sat down and we talked it over,
And now, I won't —do—o—o— it NO—O—O—O MORE!

No—o—o, I won't do it NO——O——O——O M-O-R-E!

"Donald's Blues" became a focus in Donald's sessions. He sang it with great flare, giving it a real bluesy sound, with embellishments that he had a natural feeling for. It was a tremendous emotional outlet for him and an exceptional expression of his musical talent. We recorded it on the tape recorder, and Donald performed it at a talent show.

But what is most significant, Donald internalized this song. An improvement in his impulse control generalized to other areas of his life. *And, he never did slam the door in my face anymore.*

NELL SINGS OUT GLEEFULLY

A person who has lost the use of an arm due to a stroke may be highly motivated to reactivate that limb by playing an instrument, whereas there might be resistance to physical therapy. This was true of Nell who lost the use of her right arm as well as the ability to speak. Also, both legs were in a weakened state.

Before the stroke, twenty-eight-year-old Nell, a high-functioning, mildly retarded person was ambulatory, had fairly good motoric skills, and her speech was somewhat slurred yet intelligible. Her spirit was bright and cheerful. Her lusty laughter rang through the living quarters. She enjoyed participating in a variety of activities, especially the group music therapy sessions.

Nell lived in a State institution for developmentally disabled people. In a music therapy group for three months prior to having a stroke, her favorite activity was to play the autoharp. She loved the sensation of running her fingers over the strings while I depressed the chord bars, thus making her strumming a gratifying, musical experience. At the weekly sessions, to the accompaniment of the autoharp, we would sing any number of songs that she liked, especially "Sing" from Sesame Street. Now, wheelchair bound, these moments were the highlights of her rather bleak existence.

Although the attending staff made many attempts to convince her that physical therapy would help her, she became despondent, refusing to be taken to the physical therapy room. Exploring the possibility of an interdisciplinary approach, I suggested that the physical therapist and I work together with Nell. No such thing!. Nell was adamantly against any part of physical therapy. She would lower her head, clench her lips, kick up a storm, and stubbornly stand her ground.

On the other hand, when I arrived on the floor, carrying the autoharp, her face would light up as she lifted her head. and made sounds that were almost gleeful. I didn't have to ask her if she would like to touch or "play" the autoharp, maybe "sing." When I placed the autoharp on the tray of her wheelchair and lifted her right hand to rest inertly on the strings, I would strum so that she might feel the vibrations; and, to the tune of her favorite song, would adapt words about what we were doing. Nell's cheerful spirit was beginning to come back.

As in many instances, I used one mode of music activity to reinforce another; movement can stimulate vocalization and vocalization can stimulate movement. Concentrated work with Nell in these two modes took many months of several sessions a week to bring her to the point where sensations started to return to her left hand and arm. The sensation of the vibrating strings motivated her. As if driven by her desire to make music, she transcended her limitations. It was a banner day when she made the heroic attempt to move her arm. In close harmony with each other, making music together, I observed her arm move and her fingers tentatively but definitely strumming. I heard the sounds of the vibrating strings.

The movement of her arm and fingers came back—s - l - o - w - l - y   as she began to sing the words of her favorite song. I heard her sing out gleefully, "Sssssing————ssssssing — a ——————sssssssong."

Increasingly, Nell regained the functioning level of speech and arm movement she had had before the stroke. Each time I went to her for a music therapy session, she greeted me with a bright, smile. And, each time a rather garbled, high-pitched rush of words, "I-like-to-sing-with-you, Edi," became clearer . . .

PEDRO BREAKS HIS SILENCE:
HE WHISTLES THROUGH HIS TEETH

While pondering on how to convey the full impact of my work with Pedro, a clear vision of George Minna's "Kneeling Youth" came into my mind's eye. This extraordinary sculpture had a powerful affect on me when first I saw it, striking a deep chord that has resonated within me for years. I never leave the Museum of Modern Art without dwelling on a similar sculpture that has an inspirational quality and special poignancy for me. Pedro bears a striking resemblance to this sculpture—a Lehmbruck statue come to life.

Deeply immersed in these thoughts, I was wending my way home after a full schedule of seeing clients and teaching at New York University when suddenly my attention shifted to a sign jutting out from a building. In bold letters were the words, "Books Bought and Sold Here." This could be just the book dealer on whom I needed to unload my outdated set of Funk and Wagnall Encyclopedias. But as I stepped over the threshold of this rather musty bookshop, my eyes were drawn to a beautiful art book looming like a lone star in a dark sky. I grasped the heavy volume of *19th-Century Sculpture* (Jansen, 1985) eagerly looking through it to find Minna's statue of Pedro's "likeness" that had been in my thoughts all day. And there in all its glory was a full-paged photograph of "Kneeling Youth"—an image of an elongated figure of a kneeling youth, head bowed, torso curved inward, arms tightly folded, legs extended expressing despair. A ripple of excitement coursed through my body. What a synchronicity! As is my wont, I searched for its meaning. Now I knew that I would be able to write about Pedro. I heard myself saying these poetic lines out of the recesses of my memory—lines that gave added spark to his special place in my heart:

> There exist wreaths
> Gray ones, frightened ones . . .
>
> Deepest silence everywhere
> My heart rejoices when I weep
> And my sorrows gain voices.

Fourteen-year-old Pedro was the epitome of silent grace and sorrow. Fearful of contact, he would cower in a corner, head lowered, knees pulled to his chest, arms tightly clutching his legs. He had been a battered child. He had no speech. Reports of the speech and hearing department indicated that his oral and peripheral speech mechanisms were intact as were his labial and lingual structures. His receptive language (understanding) was good. Yet it was noted that the lack of expressive language was possibly due to brain damage to the left hemisphere. In light of his history and because test results were not conclusive, his condition may have been elective mutism or hysterical aphonia (loss of voice).

I met Pedro literally on his own ground. It was too threatening for him to be taken to an unfamiliar setting with a "stranger." For several weeks I spent time with him in the apartment where he lived, sitting on the floor near him and in dulcet singsong tones chanting: "Pedro, I am Edi. I am here to be with you—to make music with you—to sing to you." How much he understood, how aware he was of me, how much he heard, I can but wonder. He was silent, his body immobile.

From these tenuous beginnings and with every possible nonverbal assurance that he was in a safe environment, Pedro became more trusting and began to open up physically, lifting his head as I sang:

> Pedro, Pedro, do you hear me singing?
> Pedro, Pedro, do you hear me singing?
> I think Pedro has heard me singing,
> Yes, I think Pedro has heard me singing.

At a later session, Pedro and I sat opposite each other on the floor in a corner of the room, which was the position he would often resort to. I was looking into his beautiful brown eyes as I softly sang:

> Pedro and Edi are sitting here together,
> Pedro and Edi are sitting here together,
> Pedro and Edi are sitting here together,
> LA - LA - LA LA LA LAAAAAAAA . . .

Sending smiles his way when I could catch a fleeting surreptitious glance from him was a form of communicating that proved to be effective. His eyes gradually grew less haunted and glances became more frequent and more direct. In consultation with the psychologist and other staff members of the interdisciplinary team, I arranged to take him to the music therapy room. Once there, he immediately found a corner to huddle in. I sat on the floor with him, strumming the autoharp, improvising words to the melody of "Jimmy Crack Corn," a folk song that I had chosen consciously because of the content of the original lyric.

The original words are:

> Jimmy crack corn and I don't care,
> Jimmy crack corn and I don't care,
> Jimmy crack corn and I don't care,
> My master's gone away.

The improvised words became:

> Pedro, Pedro is here with me,
> Pedro, Pedro is here with me,
> Pedro, Pedro is here with me,
> And I'm singing a song for you.

When a song surfaces from a store of music I have internalized, I look for a connection. For one thing, I am folk-song oriented and have found the idiom particularly effective in my work, in that it is an uncomplicated, repetitive form of musical expression whose texts are directly related to human beings and their conditions. Consequently, a particular song that comes to me always carries some obvious or underlying significance.

What was, in this instance, the connection between "Jimmy Crack Corn" and Pedro? Was there something in the lyric that conjured up a related image of an abused person who escapes from a cruel master? Hmmmmm, maybe so. Pedro—mute, abused, defending himself from the horrific "cracks" that were heaped upon him, wanting to retreat. Was I making a farfetched analysis of my intuitive choice? The more I dwelled on it, the more sense it made. That was Pedro's song..

As sessions went on, Pedro became more enlivened. Energy began to flow into his arms, his legs, his entire being. Taking his cues, I would help him to an upright position. His feet would arch into a tiptoe stance as we emerged from the corner in which he had sought refuge. Together, we walked around the room to the now familiar tune, identifying what we were doing:

> Pedro and Edi are walking 'round the room,
> Pedro and Edi are walking 'round the room,

Pedro and Edi are walking 'round the room,
We're walking together.

La la la la la la la,
La la la la la la la,
La la la la la la la,
We're walking together.

Then Pedro would begin to hyperventilate. I came to recognize this as a sign of heightened feelings that were new for him—of enjoyment but mainly tension—when he initiated an action such as clapping his hands or skipping or strumming the autoharp.

However, there was observable change taking place. Upon handing him the autoharp, he no longer drew back in fear. If I gently tapped his hands in rhythmic patterns, he accepted my touch. My hands became friendly hands. Slowly, a shift from hyperventilating to a more purposeful action took place. I was able to take his hands and swing his arms to music, bringing a measure of equilibrium to his bewildered spirit.

It is interesting to note that a number of months later, a music therapist came to observe a session. By this time, I had gained Pedro's trust to such a degree that holding his hands and having close physical contact was well-established. As the visitor was leaving, she took me aside and expressed disapproval of what she had witnessed: "In music therapy, we don't touch clients." I dismissed this outrageous attitude with, "Where did that rule come from?"

What this therapist had to be told was that a week prior to this, while sitting opposite Pedro as he huddled in the corner, he lifted his head and, with his large, sad eyes, looked directly at me. As I quietly hummed the poignant melody of the English song, "Greensleeves," Pedro raised his arms, reached over to me, and *put his arms around me*. Tears welled up in my eyes. With utter joy, I softly sang, "Yes, Pedro, I have tears in my eyes—tears of joy." As I put my arms around him, there was deepest silence that I'm quite sure he totally understood.

In subsequent sessions, we experimented with using the autoharp in different ways. This marked a change in his involvement. He imitated the strumming movements instrumentally and the sounds vocally in a call-and-response approach that I used. I would make a sustained sound, using various syllables such as "Laaaa," "Haaaa," "Daaaa," "Moooo," that might evoke a response. That must have struck Pedro as being funny. In the middle of one of those sounds, I heard a hoarse sound coming out of his throat. He was laughing!

Can you imagine my intense emotional state at hearing Pedro emit a sound—a sound from one who had been silent since infancy, according to all available records? This was a therapist's dream come true.

Then came a another dramatic development. While we were skipping around the room to his song, *Pedro started to whistle through his teeth*. This time he had really broken through the "silent barrier" and catapulted right into the "sound barrier"! The look of satisfaction on his face was a sight I will always remember with tugs at my heartstrings. And his energy level had skyrocketed.

Thereafter, whenever we moved to music, instead of hyperventilating and becoming tense or being silent, Pedro skipped with energetic exuberance and whistled his song through his teeth.

Soon after, Pedro's father came from Florida to take him home. No further contact with him was possible—a situation that I had to accept, fervently hopeful that the gains he made have been sustained.

JENNY:
WHEWWWW—I'M GLAD I GOT THAT OFF MY CHEST

Thirty-four-year-old Jenny with paresis (partial paralysis) of her right side, body bent, head on the side, nasal slow belabored speech, awkward gait, dragging of right leg—none of this stopped Jenny. She was an assertive, yes, aggressive, personality who dominated, wherever possible, the "scene of action." Being the center of attention was her style of existence. You knew when Jenny was present. Unmistakable, endearing Jenny.

Another casualty of Willowbrook, information about her history was sparse. Despite that lack, it was obvious that music therapy would address her physical condition as well as her need to override others. This treatment modality would enhance her awareness of her *unawareness* of those less able to assert themselves. Her feelings were very available to her and she expressed them freely with little regard for others. Indeed, Jenny was known to be quite a character.

In group sessions Jenny often interrupted the flow of the process, bursting forth in her inimitable way with what sounded like a cross between a laugh and a cry, and at other times calling out in high nasal tones: "Edi, Edi, I have to tell something that happened to me. Edi, Edi, I have to tell you."

Because we had a solid relationship—Jenny trusted me implicitly—I was able to handle these attention-getting bursts of energy in ways that were satisfying for her. For example, at a session when photographs were being taken, she, in her completely uninhibited manner, flirted with and smiled at the photographer, actually cooed directly at him and sang in a loud raucous voice to attract his attention. Yes, Jenny added spice to life at MDC.

I saw Jenny on an individual as well as a group basis. A song that struck a deep chord in Jenny was the spiritual, "Sometimes I Feel Like a Motherless Child." It is one of my favorites also and I had used it in a group sessions that Jenny was in. She remembered it, an at her next individual session asked me to play and sing it for her. While doing so, I noticed a change come over her. She became unusually subdued. I could hear her humming along with me. And then tears rolled down her cheeks. She was sitting close to me at the piano so I leaned over to her, and as I finished the song, a long sigh—almost a moan—came from her throat. "Edi," she uttered hoarsely, "those words—those words—

feel like a motherless—I can't remember—Edi, sing it for me again." Jenny sobbed from the depths of her heart. Her broken heart? I held her until she became calm and the tears had stopped running down her cheeks. I helped her wipe away the tears, drying her cheeks. She then flung her head back, a smile broadening her mouth. "Whewwww! I'm glad I got that off my chest!"

Information about Jenny's relationship with her mother was not available. I had a strong sense that this song was another instance of an intuitive/synchronistic choice that embodies mysterious aspects of this process we call music therapy. It is important to understand, as pointed out in a previous chapter, that this treatment modality is an art and a science. The theoretical foundations and scientific research of the total organismic or holistic effects of music on the human being—psychologically, physiologically, mentally, psychosocially, spiritually—and the methodology and techniques that are used in purposeful, conscious ways to accomplish individual and group goals are all concerns of the music therapist.

In our individual sessions, what evolved was playing "duets" on the piano. The treatment plan was to provide means of having Jenny gain use of her left hand, a fervent desire that she expressed. Whenever and however a person can enter into his or her own treatment process—even point out specific goals—the therapist must be ready, willing, and, we trust, able to fulfill these needs, wants, or potential capabilities. Jenny wanted to be able to use her left hand. She didn't put any limitations on the possibility that this could happen. (Therein is a lesson for us all.) She knew what she wanted and there was no stopping her. I was there to help her realize her dream. What better way than through the medium of piano duets.

As with everything that she did, Jenny applied herself with gusto and intense purpose. I arranged two half-hour individual sessions for her and we set to work on her impressive goal. At first, we would sit at the piano together and I would wait while she struggled to lift her left hand to the keyboard with her right hand. Her determination was unflagging. Over a period of a month, she gained more facility. When her two hands were on the keyboard, I would support her musically, playing a number of different songs that she liked, or improvising a rhythmic pattern that would stimulate her energy and musical sensibilities. For example, I would play a vigorous rhythmic pattern and contrast it with music that was soft, lyrical, and melodic. Jenny was in a constant state of what can most accurately be described as ecstasy. Every time, with my acknowledgment and encouragement, that she produced sounds that began to have a musical quality, she would exclaim with an enchantingly uninhibited expression of self-appreciation and awareness of her accomplishment, "Edi, I did it. I did it." Of course, I in turn would enthusiastically express my delight.

News of Jenny's tremendous strides was not confined to the music therapy room. When I took her to her living quarters after one especially successful session, Jenny, like a town crier, walked around the apartment announcing in her most strident tones, "I can play the piano with both hands. Edi and I played together. I can play with both hands. See, I can lift my left hand now."

The results of this treatment modality were fully appreciated by other staff members. Jenny was now able to be more independent in her daily life. Her ability to dress herself, eat with less help from the staff, and hold and grasp objects such as paper used in special education classes, all were evidence of an improved state of general functioning. This kind of transfer of gains to living skills is the ultimate goal of treatment.

Jenny, I'm so glad you got that off your chest!

JOEY: KUMM—BA—YAAAAAA

Here again, the art and science of music therapy wove its miraculous web!

A plan of treatment is formulated through an assessment of a person's history, condition, observations, and medical diagnosis. The music therapist evaluates the person from these many angles, maps out a treatment plan consisting of long- and short-term goals and determines whether the treatment will be in a group or individual session or both. In broad strokes, the science of music therapy is based on methodology and processes that involve a complex of choices of music materials, techniques, and strategies to accomplish goals. The art of music therapy encompasses the skilled and intuitive use of our therapeutic tool—music. The amalgam requires the conscious awareness and experiencing of ourselves, others, and the environment on the many diverse levels of " being human": our creativity, which involves the courage to take risks; our willingness to be exploratory, experimental, and inventive; our openness to imaginative and intuitive facets of the music therapy process; our receptivity and responsiveness to clients as complex, often unpredictable beings; our attitude toward the limitless possibilities of their potential whatever their presenting limitations may be or thought to be; our individual style and ability to project ourselves musically.

I am aligned with modern humanistic psychology that embraces and is concerned with human beings holistically: their spontaneity, humor, warmth, courage, ability to love, sense of responsibility; their quest for autonomy, self-actualization, positive interpersonal relations.

The self-examinating, self-exploratory process that I go through constantly—and in this instance that led to choosing "Kum Ba Ya" as Joey's Contact Song—is always an uplifting, enlightening, peak experience. When a song becomes the catalyst for the first reciprocal communication that is initiated by the client, the relationship that begins to take root is truly a miracle.

Joey is paraplegic, functioning on the moderate mentally retarded level. Another casualty of Willowbrook, wheelchair-bound thirty-three-year-old Joey had only the use of his left arm and could whisper a few words that were intelligible to the practiced ear. His main means of communication was shakes of

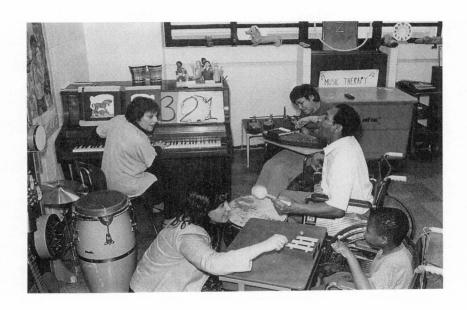

approval or disapproval of his head, or a look that would express "yes" or "no." His receptive language was within what might be called a normal range

How I "discovered" the inner Joey was an exciting exploratory series of revelations. In the first weeks of sessions, I sang and played and improvised music with words that identified who we were and what we were doing using a strategy that I devised—Identification—as a means of awakening awareness of himself and another. Establishing a client-therapist relationship with him involved finding a musical connection with him. What? When? How? I looked for the minutest indication of arousal. As yet, no music that I sang or played had any observable effect. He gave no sign of response emotionally or physically. Nothing, at least, to the naked eye. And then it happened!

When I played and sang the Nigerian song "Kum Ba Ya" Joey smiled a broad smile and flung his head back in a gesture of joy. How did this happen? Can we explain a miracle? All I can say is that somewhere, somehow, in the recesses of my being, I had a strong sense that this would be Joey's song—Our Contact Song—a song that would be the basis for establishing and building a therapeutic relationship emanating from a deeply human intuitive source. Joey was awake—awakened—vibrating—alive! In a superhuman effort, he had thrown his head back and had begun to phonate with vigor and enthusiasm. He had begun to sing with me!

> KUMMMMMM—BAAAA——-YAAAAAAAAAAA
> KUMMMM ——BAAAAA—YAAAAAAAAAA

And I sang back:

> Joey, Joey, is singing Kum ba ya,
> Joey and Edi are singing Kum ba ya,
> Joey and Edi are singing Kum ba ya,
> O Lord, Kum ba ya.

We repeated these syllables over and over. Joey's face was lit up. His eyes sparkled. His mouth opened wide. His lips formed the syllables. He was animated, energized. He didn't tire of the repetition. In fact, he didn't want to stop. He knew something very special had happened. And I knew we had discovered Our Contact Song. We were both overjoyed.

He was now awakened. This was the first stage of *A Continuum of Awareness*. The second stage was a heightening of awareness that would lead to purposeful action. Another way of expressing this human phenomenon in terms of therapy is the "cycle of awareness"—sensations leading to awareness that ultimately give rise to action. In Joey's case, the sensations aroused by "Kum Ba Ya" reached a sympathetic vibration in him, a synchronous chord that inspired him to express himself in an action that was actually a surprise to him in its newness, its unfamiliarity. When he flung his head back, he looked absolutely dazzled.

For me, the caring music therapist, totally involved in the welfare and well-being of another human being and his process of growth and development and fulfillment, it signaled the beginning of a possible transformation of Joey's life.

With developmentally disabled people, repetition—a law of learning for everyone—is particularly important. So repeat we did—using Joey's name and adapting "Kum Ba Ya" to the here-and-now person—his vocal, motoric, and emotional needs and wants, Our Contact Song can be likened to the musical form theme and variations. Using it as a basis for myriad music activities and experiences, the improvisations and adaptations of the music and lyrics are limitless. They are as inventive as the therapist and the client are for not only do the variations come from the therapist, but the client is always encouraged to contribute. As an example, Kathy (see p. 101), who had no speech available to her, communicated and entered into the creative process by means of gestures, movement, facial expression, and sounds. So too with Joey at first. As he gained the ability to phonate and sing actual words, he began to initiate a variety of emotional states that lent themselves to variations on the theme:

> Joey is smiling, oh yes
> Joey is smiling, Kum ba yaaaa
> Joey is smiling, oh yes,
> Kum–ba–ya, Kum–ba——yaaaaaaaaa

Joey is humming. Joey is moving his right arm. Joey is holding the drumstick. Joey is beating the drum. Joey and Edi are playing together. Joey and Edi are having fun together, and so on.

In the beginning stage, we would sing in a call-and-response style with Joey coming in on "Kum ba ya" at the end of each line:

> *Edi:* Joey is singing,
> *Joey:* Kum——ba——yaaaaaaa,
> *Edi:* Joey is singing,
> *Joey:* Kum——ba——yaaaaaaa,
> *Edi:* Joey is singing,
> *Joey:* Kum——ba——yaaaaaaa,
> *Joey & Edi:* O Lord, Kum——ba——yaaaaaaaa.

As he became more and more secure in his ability to phonate, his voice grew stronger and clearer and closer to the tonality of the song in the key of F major, which was well within his vocal range. He derived great pleasure from the growing awareness that his sounds were becoming more musical. In fact, he fairly bellowed out at times, his neck stretched, his head flung back, his face aglow.

And there I was, giving him the acknowledgment and acceptance that nurtured his sense of self and well-being. It was my unconditional regard and acceptance of who and what Joey was that, for the first time in his existence, gave him to himself. He felt it. He knew it. And he flourished with this nourishment. There were no wrongs. He never heard me say, "No, Joey, that's not the way to do it. Always, he heard, "Joey, you're singing the words more clearly. Joey, that sounds better, Joey, you lifted your right arm— how great. Joey, you're beating the drum." Yes, this acknowledgment of his genuine progress verbally as well as in song was health-giving—nurturing his very being. Not only did I acknowledge him, I also matched/reflected what he was doing. This approach or technique was an even deeper kind of acknowledgment of who he was. A prime example of that was what ensued as the treatment became increasingly effective.

A new phase of the therapy began with the improved use of his right arm and hand as manifested by his ability to grasp a drumstick (I attached it to his wrist with a strip of Velcro), I asked Joey if he would like to beat a drum while I played the piano. Can you imagine his excitement? He nearly jumped out of his wheel-chair.

The quality and suitability of the musical instrumentarium required for music therapy is an important aspect of the work. I placed a large Orff timpani drum with a large drumming surface that stands on adjustable legs to the right of his wheel-chair, the position and height comfortable for Joey to reach. At first his drumming, supported by my piano, was erratic, spastic, uncontrolled. However, in reflecting and matching Joey's drumming, he began to gain more control. Gradually, after many sessions, as his confidence increased his drumming became more rhythmic. The day we sang and played "Kum Ba Ya" to Joey's firm, steady beat on the drum, his joy was a joy to behold! Indeed, *our* joy was a joy to behold!

A significant development occurred in Joey's life as a result of music therapy treatment. One day, Elaine Magidson, the director of special education who was also a drama therapist, sought me out, excitedly exclaiming, "Edith, guess what happened with Joey today. I must say you can be *very* proud of what music therapy has done for him. At the rehearsal of the play we're putting on tonight, we were singing and doing movements. Well, Joey, who had always sat quietly and silently in his wheelchair just looking on, suddenly burst out singing and flung his right arm into the air. What a sense of self-gratification he had on his face! He actually seemed to be saying, 'Look at me Look what I can do!' I could hardly believe what I was seeing. I couldn't wait to tell you."

To effect this kind of transfer—to assist a person's functioning on higher and more gratifying levels of daily living—that is the underlying goal of music therapy (and certainly my conscious intention).

RAMIE LOVES SCHUBERT'S "AVE MARIA"

Where did Ramie hear Schubert's "Ave Maria"? How many times had he heard it sung? It was mystifying. The staff wasn't able to enlighten me. All I know is that at one of his group therapy sessions, he came up to the piano, stood upright, his chest thrust forward in a stance that gave the impression of one about to give an important performance, and started to sing this classic. How wonderful! I was truly touched by his deeply-felt rendition. (And I was thankful that he had chosen a song—nameless to him—that I knew well enough to support him on the spot!)

A high-functioning adult resident in his thirties, Ramie was a member of a group of eight clients who met once a week in the evening after a day at a sheltered workshop. All were verbal and enjoyed sessions where the main group goals focused on socialization and interpersonal relations. They brought in recordings that they liked, engaged in social dancing, talked about issues of their daily living; they were free to express feelings about what troubled them. If there were any deep-seated personal problems, I would see them in individual therapy.

Ramie was usually shy. Though I encouraged him to participate in singing activities, he had always held back. He had never shown any inclination to sing, or for that matter, to enter into any of the activities. He sometimes would just stand on the sidelines watching. Had he, I wonder, been singing this song "undetected" all along?

At the next session, Ramie again approached me at the piano. This time, in his soft-spoken manner, he told me that he would like to sing on Friday night. I was absolutely delighted. "Ramie, that's fantastic! Would you like to sing 'Ave Maria' at the next Home Talent Night? (There were so many miraculous things happening in the music therapy program that I instituted a once-a- month Friday evening musical program at which clients shared their special talents with the entire residency including staff and administration, as well as family and friends.) Right then and there, he went into his performance mode. The group, along with the aides who assisted at the sessions, listened in amazement to the shy Ramie they had grown accustomed to singing with such unabashed pleasure. It was a most extraordinary happening. No one, but no one, had ever had the slightest idea that he had this secret love of singing.

Before his appearance at Home Talent Night, I arranged to have Ramie come to the music therapy room for rehearsals. With each rehearsal his singing became fuller and more expressive. On the big night, he performed with aplomb and the audience responded with appreciative applause. It was an auspicious occasion for Ramie. He was the star performer of the evening. And, although we may make the assumption that he wasn't aware that he chose to sing music of very highest caliber, it may well be an erroneous assumption. It's possible that somewhere in the deep recesses of his being, Ramie did know. He certainly knew that it was a beautiful song and you could *feel* how much he loved to sing it. To the entire staff's surprise, he started to assert himself with a newfound sense of self-esteem and self-worth. He was a changed person.

This account exemplifies the importance of the qualified music therapist's capacity to meet the needs and interests of the many and diverse clients encountered in the practice of music therapy. The requirements for entering the profession and the training to become a practitioner involve being able to handle, in the best way possible, a situation such as is described here. This is not to say that we music therapists have to know *all* music ever written. What it does say is that we must have a broad musical foundation and repertoire to use in ways that enhance the health and well-being of the people we are giving service to. We must be able to tap the healthy areas that exist in all human beings—to tap into their wellness.

LORENZO DANCES OUT OF HIS SHELL

Lorenzo was thirty-eight years of age when he first came to therapy as part of a group of mildly retarded, high-functioning persons. For the seven months that he had been coming, there was no evidence of interest in what was going on, no contact with others in the group, no contact with me. He would enter the room, his face somewhat animated, rush to take the same seat each time, and then revert to his usual sullen, set stance—head bowed, shoulders hunched, body lifeless.

What contradictions, what conflicts, what desires were seething inside him? Once in the room, he had never shown observable signs of wanting to participate in the group process. Yet he came willingly. Other than the few expletives that he spurted at rare moments—which I reflected to let him know that I was there for him—he had no speech available for communicative purposes and presented an impenetrable resistance to contact. In fact, the first time I had made a move to take his hands, he recoiled with visible distress, his shoulders more hunched and closed in than ever. He seemed to just want to "be there."

Very good. If that was a source of well-being for him, that was fine with me. If just being there in a musical, caring environment was enough, seeing others play instruments and sing and dance, that's what was right for him. *There were no conditions on his being there.* Maybe one day the music and a sense of my caring would bring him out of his shell. Maybe he'd be able to communicate—to express—what was going on inside him. Maybe.

Because I put no ceiling on the possibilities of a person's potential, whatever that individual's condition is, I am always on the alert for that shift in perception that can occur in a flash—a shift that might have been incubating for months, even years, and manifests in a transformative moment.

May I remind you, dear reader, that you are imagining yourself peeking through a one-way mirror, perhaps hardly noticing Lorenzo who had not shown any sign of wanting to participate in the music therapy process. The session that the seven other clients had been engaged in had been rather low-key yet intense based on improvisational use of a variety of melodic percussion instruments such as Orff xylophones, a marimba, and tone bells. We had been working on group as well as individual goals, expressing emotions, such as anger, that they were aware of experi-

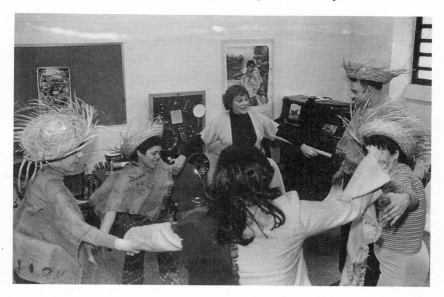

encing or had been unable to express verbally or in nondestructive ways. A goal was to raise awareness on a continuum in order to handle anger peaceably.

Bringing this to a close, I thought to change the pace and play a rhythmic, stimulating Trinidadian love song, "Roo Koo Bay." Everyone in the group except Lorenzo selected a drum or Latin percussion instrument. I gave forth on the piano.

Singing these simple syllables in the key of D minor and drumming the repetitive rhythmic pattern, we chanted melodically and rhythmically, over and over, in fast and slow tempos, in soft and loud dynamics:

> Roo koo bay,
> Roo koo bay,
> Roo koo bay.

Then as the group danced in a circle, like an arrow, Lorenzo flew out of his chair, his entire being alive with the excitement of the music. He started to dance intricate steps in perfect rhythm, flinging his arms in the air, vigorously moving in the style of Flamenco dancing. He laughed joyously as I sang in the rhythm and tune of "Roo koo bay":

> Lorenzo is dancing,
> Lorenzo is dancing,
> To Roo koo bay.

We all sang with enthusiasm:

> Lorenzo is dancing,
> Lorenzo is dancing,
> To Roo koo bay

From that momentous happening on, Lorenzo was an active member of the group and took every opportunity possible to "display" his hidden talent. When the staff heard of this phenomenon, there were requests for him to entertain at parties in his apartment. His sense of self-worth had no bounds. The expletives were replaced with words that he used consciously to identify some of his needs and wants. The staff worked together with me, using records and live music on a daily basis, assisting him to soar above the ceiling that had for so long kept him from realizing his true self.

PETER AND I WEAR RAINCOATS
TO ONE-TO-ONE SESSIONS

Knowing of my music-therapy-rescue-mission reputation, the teacher of the public school that Peter was attending and the staff of Manhattan Developmental Center where he was living called me, frantically requesting—pleading—that I take fourteen-year-old Peter for one-to-one music therapy. The situational crisis—his spitting at and on other students, teachers, anyone within spitting distance—had reached disastrous proportions. Bright, loquacious, defiant, spiteful, "spitful" Peter was in danger of being suspended.

I must say that the prospect of dealing with this particular problematic circumstance was not exactly the image I had of being a music therapist. What image did I have? Actually, until this "problem in living"—in Thomas Szaaz's terms (1974)— was added to the store of knowledge I had been accumulating for eight years, I hadn't once thought of having an image as a music therapist. Yes, I had given much thought to my identity. But image? No! That never entered my mind. And here I was, faced with a rather distasteful problem that certainly fit my identity, which in my "book" meant treating and dealing with as many kinds of human conditions as possible. Certainly the challenges of children with early childhood autism and the severely, multiply-handicapped were far greater than dealing with the behavior that Peter was exhibiting.

Of course, this was symptomatic of deeper problems. However, it is a sad commentary that the more exaggerated Peter's behavior became, the more the teachers, staff, and peers had rejected him and openly shown their distaste. This, as I observed, exacerbated the situation. Resistance to Peter was causing persistence and he was being referred to me for help—for relief. The matter of an image—of being spat on and at—wasn't the consideration. A young person was in trouble. He needed caring, loving acceptance, and understanding.

Peter was well aware of the annoyance (to put it mildly) that large wads of spit were causing . He had an endless supply. This was not a compulsive action. It was deliberately designed to cause disturbance. Not only was he aware, he was enjoying making everyone and anyone in his presence suffer. He was having fun. He laughed with delight at the reactions he was getting. And the attention. Nothing else he had tried had worked so well. This was really paying off!

I arranged a daily half-hour session for as long as it would take to stabilize his status at school, making as many inquiries about him as time would allow. The approach was phenomenological—here and now—inasmuch as the urgency of his precarious position at school needed immediate action on my part. Now, it was a question of finding ways to have Peter enter into his own therapy process—to find ways to have him aware of the goal of eliminating this behavior that was interfering in his relations with his peers as well as teachers, *interfering in his life.*

At our first session, as I explored kinds of music and musical activities that he might like, I became well acquainted with the presenting problem. He tested my endurance. I geared myself to endure. How it would work out I wasn't quite sure. Interestingly enough, one song that I discovered was a favorite of his and one that came closest to being Our Contact Song was the Sesame Street song, "I Like Trash " (1971). Was this revealing something about Peter?

We wove an activity around this song, acting it out, playing a variety of instruments to my piano, he singing with gusto. Peter's highly-developed sense of humor was very much in evidence. We were making good contact through making music together. However, the spitting continued to be unrelenting. I decided then and there to wear a protective garment at the next session. I brought a raincoat in the next day.

My wearing a raincoat was a sign of acceptance of the situation, not approval of it. Peter understood the distinction. He even joined in what became a joke between us. He wore his raincoat the next day. With this resolution of the issue of being inundated by a rain of spit, the therapy began to "take." As we improvised music, identifying what he was doing in lyrics to songs, the need to act out lessened. Peter was feeling the unconditional regard for him as a human being yet was aware of the unacceptable behavior that isolated him and made him unlovable. Happily, I can report that over a period of two months his status in school became secure—the threat of suspension was removed.

This is not to say that music therapy in depth would not have been indicated. In my view, it most certainly was. However, circumstances did not permit. And before bringing this anecdotal account to an end, I wish to have it clearly understood that *I did not at any moment use the strategy Reflection to make contact with Peter. . . .*

THE MAKING OF AN LP ALBUM

I had been conducting music therapy sessions for two years when in 1975 I conceived of the idea of the record album that evolved into *Music Adapted, Composed, and Improvised by Edith Hillman Boxill, C.M.T. for Music Therapy with the Developmentally Handicapped*, Folkways Record FX6180 (1976). This was a rather cumbersome title but one thought to be indicative of the unique nature of the album: A resource and an instructional guide for practicing music therapists as well as music therapy students, illustrating and suggesting ways of using music in the music therapy process. There was no question in my mind that Folkways Records* would be the most suitable recording company for a recording of this nature. The response of Moses Asch, the president of Folkways was immediate and enthusiastic. After much discussion of alternative approaches to this project, instead of the traditional approach of presenting the music alone, I came up with the notion of having clients that I had been working with—various developmentally disabled persons—participate in the recording, singing and playing instruments just as they did in actual music therapy sessions.

Mr. Asch thought it brilliant, particularly in light of the nature of Folkways Records. Although we knew that this was a venture of an experimental nature and would take careful planning, we didn't for a minute doubt its ultimate success and potential to make a contribution to the field of music therapy. Never before in the industry had developmentally disabled people recorded on a commercial label. It would be the first in the world!

Six clients, ranging in age from seventeen to twenty-nine, were selected based on their familiarity with the music that I had chosen to include on the album, having sung and played the material in music therapy sessions. Criteria were also their level of development, their ability to function in a different environment, and on their capacity to understand the nature of this event. Two of the clients had accumulated a collection of records that any teenager would envy and were really excited about going to a studio where records are made. The others were accustomed to going on trips such as specific concerts, the circus, and Macy's Thanksgiving parade. However, because there are preconceived assumptions and generalizations about people who are developmentally disabled (or, as usually thought of, mentally retarded), this was a drastic departure from any recording situation that the manager of the studio had ever been "confronted" with. Imagine having *mentally retarded* people recording in a recording studio! Both Mr. Asch and I assured him that his studio would not be in shambles! And I must say that what transpired was an eye-opener for the manager, the engineer, and the entire studio staff.

This trip was one that everyone involved will long remember. I planned it as a treat on Valentine's Day, February 14, 1976, explaining the idea to the clients in this way: "We'll start with a ride in a van to go to a place where we'll be singing and playing instruments just the way we sing and play and sometimes record on the tape recorder in the music therapy room. At the place called a recording studio, we'll be recording so that we'll be able to hear ourselves on a *real* record. What do you think? Do you think that *that* will be special? And then we'll go to a restaurant to have lunch." They loved going on trips and this one did sound *very* special to them—a special holiday treat.

With the help of my assistant music therapist, a music therapy intern, and a member of the staff of Manhattan Developmental Center, we loaded the van with a conga drum, a timpani drum, a variety of Latin percussion instruments, an autoharp, and a xylophone. We were then set for our ten o'clock appointment at the studio for what I thought was to be a "dry run"—a rehearsal—in order to acquaint the clients with the environment, what they would be doing, and how I would present the content of the album—the order of the music and approach that would produce the desired results. The actual recording session was to be at a later date.

Time requirements of twenty minutes per side were stipulated. I designed a structure that would give shape and balance to the album and at the same time meet these constraints. Would I achieve the intention and purpose—capture the aliveness and spontaneity that is characteristic of the music therapy process rather than be obliged to follow a format of a traditional recording? Would I be locked into a formula that the engineer might require?

All these concerns were quickly dissipated. What took place was an unforgettable phenomenon. From the moment we started to record to the final note, the clients were comfortable, beautifully responsive, and actively enjoying themselves. They sang, played, moved, and applied themselves with purposeful and focused energy. We were doing and being what was natural for us—what was uniquely ours. It was working like a charm: the pacing, the timing, the order of the music as I envisioned it were all coming together. Everyone made connections that resulted in a successful endeavor: the clients with the studio, the engineer with the clients, the manager with all of us. Not only did the sequence of the music add up to twenty minutes per side—almost to the second!—the spontaneous, alive spirit that was so critical for the nature and intention of the album came through with inspired and inspirational distinction.

Upon meeting with the engineer for possible adjustments and to discuss arrangements for the actual recording, we were absolutely incredulous (although secretly I had a feeling that it was so): something remarkable had been accomplished—the timing, the spirit, the quality, the intended "message" were all to perfection.

The "dry run" had turned out to be *the* run.

A news release was sent to the *New York Times* and the *New York Post:*

> Edith Hillman Boxill, Director of Music Therapy at
> Manhattan Developmental Services and Professor of
> Music Therapy at New York University, is the
> creator/producer of Folkways Records' recent release
> of the first and only record for music therapy with
> developmentally disabled persons (or for that matter,
> the first and only music therapy album), *Music
> Adapted, Composed, and Improvised by Edith Hillman
> Boxill, C.M.T. for Music Therapy with the Developmentally
> Handicapped.*

And, when Dr. Frank Field, science editor of NBC-TV learned of the release of this Folkways record album, he arranged to film an interview with me and a music therapy session of my clients at MDC for a television presentation on NewsCenter 4.

MDC was a beehive of excitement when Dr. Field arrived with a crew of ten cameramen and were escorted to the music therapy room. While the cameras were being set up, Dr. Field and I exchanged and explored ideas as to possible ways of handling this unusual news "item." I came up with the suggestion that as an introductory feature, a mock session with Dr. Field as a client might be an interesting approach. "Yes, it might be interesting, but oh no," was Dr. Field's immediate and rather amused response. However, a moment later he said, with a thoughtful smile," On second thought, let's try it." And, of the two-hour filming, that segment (which can be said to have been unique and enjoyable for both "client" and therapist and one that made the therapy process "real" for Dr. Field) was among the segments that were aired several weeks later.

Eight clients who were selected to be filmed were inspiring to see and hear as they sang and played "Guantanamera" on conga drums, bongos, and Latin percussion instruments to the rhythms that I played on the piano. The camera crew *almost* forgot (as they said afterward) that these were people with developmental disabilities. Dr. Field declared of the occurrence, "It certainly exemplifies the benefits and importance of the treatment modality—music therapy. I wish to congratulate Edi Boxill for her dedicated work. I hope to do a follow-up filming of a full session one day." Although that didn't quite come off, my gratitude goes out to Dr. Field for his interest in music therapy and his awareness of the need to bring this treatment modality to the attention of the public at large.

The program was aired in January, 1976 on a Friday at 6:00 P.M. An incident that not only amused me but proved the value of this exposure took place the next afternoon. While at the Museum of Modern Art, as I was absorbed in viewing one of the statues on exhibit, my eyes were literally pulled toward two people pointing at me with a conspiratorial look of recognition, their heads nodding in a gestural "yes." They had evidently seen the NBC program.

And then, in addition to a review in the American Association for Music Therapy (AAMT) Newsletter, this album received further professional acclaim in a review by Kenneth Bruscia, Ph.D., Professor of Music Therapy at Temple University:

> Folkways Record has just released one of the most
> unique and innovative LP albums in the field of Music
> Therapy. It is entitled *Music Adapted, Composed, and
> Improvised by Edith Hillman Boxill, C.M.T. for Music
> Therapy with the Developmentally Handicapped.* This
> album does not provide just another recorded recipe
> with step-by-step instructions for doing music therapy.
> Nor does it provide "canned music" for the uninspired

to use as music therapy. Rather, the album is a collection of sensitively recorded live music sessions with Edi and a group of clients who are having a joyous therapeutic experience. It is a collection of exquisite musical compositions adapted, composed, or improvised especially for this group. You will hear Sondheim, Short, Dietrich, and Miranda all become the inimitable Edi—a loving, beloved, and extraordinary music therapist. You will hear handicapped persons overcome their own individual difficulties and problems as they play, sing, and laugh. In short, you will hear possibly the most touching therapy you have ever experienced.

My heartfelt thanks go to Edi and her clients for sharing these experiences with us, and to Folkways Records for making it possible.

FIFTH MOVEMENT

THE TAO EXPANDS—GOING BEYOND THE TREATMENT ROOM

Never doubt that a small group of thoughtful, committed citizens can change the world. Indeed, it's the only thing that ever has.
— Margaret Mead

There are many ways to discover and rediscover the sacredness and magic of human life. At heart, all of these ways [reveal] human life as a journey and as an adventure that has no end. The journey is a quest for joining inner and outer experience, mind and body, and waking up in the reality of being genuinely human.

—Jeremy Hayward

MUSIC THERAPISTS FOR PEACE

> Music must serve a purpose; it must be a part of
> something larger than itself, a part of humanity . . .
>
> —Pablo Casals

Utterly synchronous and perfectly timed, it was in March of 1988
upon my founding Music Therapists for Peace that I got a message in a Chinese fortune cookie: *You love peace!* This message—
not new to me, but coming at that particular moment in that particular form—struck both a familiar and amusing chord in me.

As a human being and as a music therapist not only do I
love peace, I live peace, and aim to embody peace on all levels of
my existence. From earliest childhood recollections, I have always
attempted to bring people together, to help settle conflicts peaceably. Physically and emotionally repelled by abusive behavior, I
have been concerned about injustice, divisiveness, destructive
relationships, inhumanness. Throughout, music has been my
source of fulfillment and harmony and, early on, I observed that
when people sing together a spirit of relatedness and possibly joy
prevails.

The world needs new attitudes and new ways to imple-
ment peacemaking and conflict resolution. And we music therapists need to use our skills and perspectives to help bring about
the new attitudes that evoke more humane states of being. When
the approach to using music as a therapeutic agent for the betterment of humankind is within the grand context of world peace,

music therapy becomes an evolving, evolutionary process that has unlimited, unimagined possibilities. The mission of Music Therapists for Peace (MTP) is to have music therapists maintain *a conscious awareness of contributing to the healing of our wounded planet.* There is no alternative, for what if we develop our profession to the highest possible levels but do not have a world to practice it in! Let us heed Albert Einstein's words of caution that "We shall require a substantially new manner of thinking if [humankind] is to survive" (pamphlet of International Physicians for the Prevention of Nuclear War), and his words of encouragement that a critical mass of two percent of like-minded people can effect a shift in consciousness.

The broad scope and depth of the nature of music therapy is in evidence; its global possibilities for effecting healing and more harmonious relations among diverse people(s) of our planet Earth is being put into action. Over the years, my concern has been known to my colleagues. This concern about the world we live in calls for expansion of our scope and horizons by going beyond the treatment room, reaching out to people everywhere. Whenever possible, especially at national and international music therapy conferences, I expressed this perspective until these ideas became synonymous with my presence. When this vision evolved into an actual "living" entity, it was not only enthusiastically embraced but seemed to be wholly expected!

In December of 1985, while presenting at the Fifth World Congress of Music Therapy in Genoa, Italy, I was consumed with the idea that we music therapists have within us resources that not only assist the healing of individuals and groups but can bring about health to our wounded planet Earth. Over the years that followed, the seed planted in my mind-body-soul took root. Gradually sprouts pushed upward.

I had been contemplating a change in my work that would necessitate resigning from MDC. What opened up the way to the "birth" of Music Therapists for Peace was a happening that could have been a disaster in my life but that I reframed to be an opportunity: I was attacked by a highly assaultive client who was usually well-guarded but for a split second was unattended. As I lay on the corridor floor being thrashed from head to foot, I retained enough consciousness to be aware that this might precipitate the move I had thought to take. However, although this way of making a change was hardly ideal, I did make the choice to leave as director of music therapy at MDC and move on to a new phase of my journey. In fact, immediately upon the accident, I left MDC not to return. Some weeks later, after intensive treatment for the injuries I had sustained, I handed in my resignation. *In retrospect*, I think of this happenstance metaphorically and *happily* as having been in the throes of labor, ready to give birth for the fourth time: first a son, second a daughter, third a book, and now an organization!

The above incident took place in August of 1987. While recuperating, a vision of this new phase of my lifework flashed into my conscious mind: I was to found an organization to be called Music Therapists for Peace. Thinking about it, cogitating about it, deliberating about it, talking it over with colleagues, I then prepared the way to bring it forth at the next national music therapy conference of the American Association for Music Therapy in March of 1988.

In the interim, I was invited to give a presentation at a conference of Peace Through Education which was cosponsored by the United Nations University for Peace in Costa Rica and the Robert Muller School in Arlington, Texas. The latter is a very special school named for the former assistant secretary of the United Nations for forty years and current chancellor of the United Nations University for Peace. The core curriculum of the school is based on world peace and is attended by children from birth to high school age.

A peak experience was in store for me at this conference: A song I had written entitled "Song of Peace for the Children" was to be offered as a peace meditation at the opening of the final ceremony of the conference at which Dr. José Arguelles was to be the keynote speaker. I was already a devotee of Dr. Arguelles, having read his remarkable book, *The Mayan Factor*, and knowing him to be the creator of Harmonic Convergence, a global meditation for peace that had taken place at sunrise on August 17, 1987. My involvement in this phenomenon had been intense.

I had set the "Song of Peace for the Children" to an anonymous untitled poetic text that was in a packet of Harmonic Convergence material. An instantaneous flash of connectedness engulfed me when I read the text; I thought, I *have* to set it to music For several months, this awareness that there was something special I needed to *do* kept tugging at my heart. Then one Sunday afternoon in June, Don Campbell, music educator and friend, came to visit with me in my home. I told him of my dream to write a song for Harmonic Convergence. Fortuitously enough, Don was involved in the satellite broadcast celebrating this event that was to emanate from Boulder, Colorado. Fully committed to following my dream, I promised to send him a recording of the music for possible inclusion in the broadcast. Inspired to put this into action, the moment he took leave of me I sat down at my Steinway Grand, sounded the note F (which I learned later is a *sacred tone of the universe*) on the keyboard, stretched the fingers of both hands in a sonorous chord of D flat major (which I recently have been told is a *sacred scale of the universe*), and from there a tonal meditation evolved. This passionate moment of inspiration was followed by the work to transform the text into musical form. I had a rough draft to show him the very next day that I entitled:

SONG OF PEACE FOR THE CHILDREN
A BLESSING WAY CHILDREN'S PRAYER FOR THE EARTH

O Earth,
Make a blessingway for the children,
Show them a path that is free.
Make them a blessingway that is free of war,
Show them a path that is free of war!

O Earth,
Make a blessingway for the children,
Send them a path where they may walk free,
And the stars will make bright each step of
        the blessingway,
Show them a path that is free of war!

Free of war between brother and brother,
Free of war between sister and sister,
Free of war between family and family,
Free of war between nation and nation.

O Earth,
Show the children a planet that is free of war forever,
Send them a new dawn where the light is the color of love
And let them hear the song and the sounds of PEACE . . .
PEACE . . . PEACE . . . PEACE . . . PEACE . . .

SONG OF PEACE FOR THE CHILDREN

The Blessingway Children's Prayer for the Earth

Edith Hillman Boxill

Make them   a   bless-ing-way   that is   free of war!____   Show them a path____   that is
stars   will make bright   each step of that bless-ing-way,____   Show them a path____   that is

free of war!
free of war!

subito **pp** *(very gradual cresc. and accel.)*

Free of war   be - tween broth - er   and   broth- er,____

Free of war   be - tween sis- ter and   sis - ter,____   Free of war   be - tween fam - i- ly and

ad infinitum...

Then came the recording—voice and piano with a flute obligato—that had been requested for the satellite broadcast, the very one now being played as a prelude to Dr. Arguelles' keynote address, the very one that emerged as the Contact Song of Music Therapists for Peace.

I had searched for the author of the poem that had struck such a resonant chord in my being. The search was to no avail. However, because of the nature of the text whose essence is a plea for a "blessingway for the children," I thought it might be a Native American prayer. That was one possibility but I was never sure.

I had announced to the audience of at least a thousand that what they were about to experience was a musical meditation for peace. I explained that I called it "Song of Peace for the Children." When it was finished, Dr. Arguelles was introduced. After rendering an invocation on a wooden flute, he said, " I was very moved by what I just heard. I wrote those words. "Can this be true? Am I imagining this? Did I hear Dr. Aguelles say that he wrote those words?" Yes! yes! He had said that he often sent out writings of this nature anonymously.

When he finished his presentation, I rushed over to him, expressing my joy at having "found" him! A knowing smile from Dr. Aguelles was followed by a warm embrace. He, too, was profoundly affected by the synchronicity of this discovery. I knew even more strongly that Music Therapists for Peace would be born.

A longtime practice of mine was to consult the Chinese philosophical treatise *The I Ching or Book of Changes* for guidance. I now turned to it to help find out what kind of action to take, what kind of statement to make, how to put out the word about MTP. I was influenced by the psychoanalyst C. G. Jung who tells us that upon receiving an invitation to write a Foreword to the Bollingen Series XIX of *The I Ching* (1968), he consulted the original *I Ching* for guidance. For me, guidance came in the form of the Image of Ching/The Well—hexagram #48. Taking off with these excerpts, I announced the founding of Music Therapists for Peace:

> In the well is a clear, cold spring. . . . One draws from
> the well without hindrance . . . supreme good fortune.
> . . . The all-important thing about a well is that its
> water be drawn . . . The well is there for all. . . . It has a
> spring and never runs dry. . . . (p. 188)

This image was synchronous with my vision for MTP. The message that it would be a movement—a network—rather than a membership organization in the customary sense was conveyed metaphorically *that the well is there for all*. It was to be a global network that belongs to all music therapists. A critical mass of like-minded music therapists that would be dedicated to bringing people together in peace on individual, group, community, and ultimately, global, levels.

And so, after many years of gestation, Music Therapists for Peace was born on March 18,1988 in Boston, Massachusetts at a national conference of the American Association for Music Therapy. As word of its arrival spread throughout the conference, there was a growing realization that something quite extraordinary had occurred: that this was an outer manifestation of congruency with the inherent peacemaking nature of music therapy and its far-reaching implications for going beyond the treatment room out to the many and diverse people(s) of planet Earth, I was greeted with, "Of course! Of course! It's a natural." What music therapists immediately became aware of was that the very nature of music therapy is that of peacemaking and that we are already doing the work of peace. *But how many of us know it?*

In essence, this was a "wake up call" to music therapists around the world as to the urgency of utilizing our powerful treatment modality to make a conscious contribution to the health and healing of our planet. It was a call to explore possibilities for expanding the scope of our work, a call to give unprecedented service and create peaceful, harmonious relations between people(s) through a universal means of expression—music. For, with this awakening, this awareness, this knowing, would come a transformational perspective and attitude that would expand the scope of our work and advance an evolutionary shift in our consciousness—a shift that would mean taking a leap into the future—to new and unexplored territory, carrying the message that *peace is not only possible, it is imperative.*

Yes, the work and mission of MTP would transcend organizational affiliations and would not only welcome but initiate opportunities for helping bring about an evolutionary shift in our attitudes and actions. It would be a worldwide network of music therapists whose focus would be peace—peace on multicultural and multisocietal levels, peace on individual and collective levels, peace on local and global levels.

MTP'S GLOBAL CONTEXT: AN EXPANSION OF A CONTINUUM OF AWARENESS

From a clinical perspective, MTP is more than a worldwide network of like-minded music therapists. *It is a global context.* Through the conscious use of music to bring peace on all levels of existence, its enlarged scope and horizons are an expansion of the concept and application of *A Continuum of Awareness.* Implicit and explicit are the many diverse forms that music therapy can take and are already occurring globally. Creating a new paradigm within this context and applying the strategies that are the theoretical foundation of *A Continuum of Awareness*, music therapists use their individual skills, styles, and cultural heritages to encompass personal issues, conditions, and problems while expanding their own awareness of the need to deal with planetary issues, conditions, and problems. For this context gives breadth and depth and enlarged dimension to our work. It engages the music therapist actively in changes that transform thinking, reduce violent and destructive behaviors, and nurture the well-being and wellness of humans and nonhumans. It means "being peace"—"thinking peace"—"living peace."

MTP inaugurated an historic event in October of 1990. It celebrated its first Universal Music Therapists for Peace Day at the United Nations in tribute to the United Nations International Day of Peace, sending out the message of "peacemaking though musicmaking." Since then, music therapists around the world have been observing this event during the third week of October, linking together in "songs and sounds of peace," with the intention of enhancing peace in the world on all possible levels. As we go into the next millennium, it is more urgent than ever that we make our voices heard far and wide—that we exert a stronger and broader influence through the benefits that our modality offers.

In sum, this global vision and orientation embodies the cross-cultural role of music therapists as "ambassadors of peace" through music therapy. Humankind is experiencing momentous changes in global communication and networking, calling for a critical mass of like-minded people to bring about a shift from outmoded, obsolete ways. Uncharted possibilities for the influence and impact of healing through music therapy are at hand. And MTP is on the leading edge of generating ideas and innovative paradigms for this expansion. An integral part of the work is acknowledging and honoring cultural differences as well as commonalities. By enveloping multicultural and cross-cultural musics and perspectives, music therapists bring a diversity of people together in significant and enriching ways.

The world is fast becoming a global village as perceived by the cultural historian Marshall McLuhan. Far-distant and disparate peoples of our planet share concerns about their mutual welfare—about the very survival of our precious home. Never before in the history of our species have we experienced living in a world that requires more awareness and understanding of the essences of humanness. What makes our modality so viable and pertinent is the fact that a basic essence of the universe common to all people is *music*, one of human's most ancient and most natural forms of expression, healing, and communication.

MTP's global context and vision offer untold possibilities for consciously using the power of music for the betterment of humankind, for the enhancement of peace in the world on all levels. Its broad scope and depth are being put into action—effecting healing and creating more harmonious relations among the many diverse people(s) of our planet Earth.

S.A.V.E. THE WORLD THROUGH MUSIC

Words and Music
Rafael Picorelli and Edith Hillman Boxill
Arranged by Ron Granger

STUDENTS AGAINST VIOLENCE EVERYWHERE—
S.A.V.E.— THROUGH MUSIC THERAPY

> If we are to reach peace in this world . . . we shall
> have to begin with the children and if they will
> grow up in their natural innocence, we won't have
> to struggle; we shall go from love to love and peace
> to peace until at last all the corners of the world are
> covered with that peace and love for which
> consciously or unconsciously the world is
> hungering.
>
> — Mahatma Gandhi

> Practicing nonviolence is first of all to become
> nonviolent. Then when a difficult situation
> presents itself we will react in a way that will help
> the situation. This applies to problem of the family
> as well as the problems of society.
>
> —Thich Nhat Hanh

One of the innovative paradigms of Music Therapists for Peace is
the pilot project Students Against Violence Everywhere—
S.A.V.E.—Through Music Therapy. A further expansion of *A Continuum of Awareness*, this project is designed *to empower students to
save their own lives.*

Recognizing the critical necessity for addressing the issue
of violence that is rampant in schools today and is taking more

virulent forms at younger and younger ages, MTP has been developing and implementing a Peace School Program: Conflict Resolution and Harmonious Relationships Through the Conscious Use of Music. As an outgrowth of this program, S.A.V.E. through Music Therapy was conceived as a preventive as well as therapeutic project that would reach children of all ages. It is a hands-on approach that provides tools for positive alternatives to destructive behaviors and actions. Dealing with feelings and impulses that can escalate into violence, the need to build a sense of self-worth is key.

The premise of the project is that *it belongs to the students* and the music therapist is a caring guide who facilitates the work. Students are encouraged to express their feelings, voice concerns, and share their dreams. In understanding the concept of the project, they are aware of the opportunity to participate actively in setting their own goals, initiating their ideas for activities, and their choices of music.

Launched in September of 1995 at the Lincoln Academy, a New York City public junior high school, a model group of eight students ranging in age from thirteen to fifteen has demonstrated the importance and efficacy of this work. Through the application of music therapy techniques and strategies, the music therapist aims to bring about transformation of attitudes and effect changes in actions that will transfer to the students' daily lives. The overall goal is to raise students' awareness of themselves: how they relate to others, how their actions affect themselves and others—how they can be actively involved "in saving their own lives." They address here-and-now feelings, behaviors, and issues, offering constructive means of relating to peers, teachers, and family through musical activities that include singing, instrument playing (such as xylophones, drums, Latin percussion), movement/dancing, and improvising words to original and composed songs. Guidelines that they themselves have established help them:

- gain self-control over destructive and impulsive behaviors
- discover ways to disagree/resolve conflict peaceably
- handle anger in constructive ways
- be aware of their tone of voice and the language they use
- understand how to share and work together
- develop a healthy sense of self/self-worth

- learn to respect themselves and others
- remember the meaning of S.A.V.E. through Music Therapy

Interventions offering alternative behaviors via musical activities are:

Impulse Control

Impulse control is basic to the problem of violence. Internalizing impulse control is a key building block of this work. A fundamental issue that requires creative approaches and solutions, lack of self-control over impulsive, often compulsive, behaviors is all too frequently manifest and the consequences dire. When impulse control is developed internally, not imposed externally, when the ability to control that first impulse to become embroiled in potentially violent encounters is recognized, the need to resort to violence can be overcome. This intervention is designed to assist students to become consciously aware of habitually experiencing their lack of impulse control in varying degrees. It is designed to bring this most critical of problems to their awareness and offer alternative ways of handling their behavior.

An initial stage of internalizing impulse control focuses on awakening levels ofawareness based on the students' active participation in their own processes of acquiring and learning to use tools:

- to establish and follow guidelines for group work
- to improve attending skills
- to consciously listen and/or maintain silence
- to consciously start and stop and wait
- to hold give-and-take conversations verbally and musically
- to work together cooperatively

Role Playing

Fully cognizant of the fact that anger and hostility are very close to the surface of many young people today, this intervention is intended to accept the gamut of feelings while providing alternative behaviors that express the emotions in ways that are not destructive and harmful. This intervention is a form of psychodrama or dramatization of the kinds of behaviors that the students have experienced themselves or have witnessed. It is designed to counteract impulsive, automatic reactions—rather than responses—to situations that very often escalate into destructive, violent actions. The intervention is designed to acknowledge the emotions that the students have—particularly anger and hostility—and to learn to handle the feelings in ways that are more acceptable, less explosive, and not harmful. Feelings such as anger are a valid, sometimes necessary means of expression. However, through the conscious use of music—a drum beating activity, for example—the angry feelings can either be sublimated, dissipated, rechanneled, or communicated in language and tone of voice that are assertive rather than aggressive

Peaceful Disagreement

Disagreements, differences of opinion, and conflicts are acceptable forms of human behavior. Awareness of this is the first step. However, what we can do about settling disagreements and resolving conflicts in more peaceful ways is the challenge. If "negotiating" can be learned and practiced on the simplest, most basic levels in the earliest years of growth and development, the possibility for negotiating that is imperative for the survival of our planet will one day be the way of nations.

Centering

This intervention is based on the music therapy process called "rhythmic entrainment" or "sympathetic vibration." As a human phenomenon, it can be said to have its origins in the African tribal tradition of a group moving in circle formation to the same rhythmic pattern. The same phenomenon occurs when stringed instruments that are side by side begin to vibrate in synchrony with each other. (Pendulum clocks have also been known to begin to swing back and forth in the same tempo.) This phenomenon is described as "locking in" or tuning in to another's beat.

Mindful Lyric Making

Mindful—consciously selective—lyric making is a valuable avenue and outlet for self-expression and creativity. It can also be a form of catharsis. Thoughts and feelings that may be either supressed or vented in asocial ways are converted into musical extemporaneous expression that can enhance awareness and self-

NO MORE GUNS...BEAT DRUMS!

awareness, knowledge and self-knowledge. When taped or written down, words and thoughts that come forth spontaneously, yet with a particular focus and meaning, can be the basis of ongoing musical activities.

The lyrics of songs are often a taking-off point for self-examination and self-awareness. Drums—bongos, congas, African talking drums—are a dominant musical instrument used and lyric writing a major music activity. A rhythmic pattern on drums along with improvised rapping are exemplified in the verses created by the students to the following song:

NO MORE GUNS . . . BEAT DRUMS!
EDITH HILLMAN BOXILL
WITH
DEBORAH GREEN

How can we have a more peaceful world,
Where we live in harmony?
How do we settle our differences

Without fighting senselessly?
We can say we're not willing
We can stop violence and killing.
NO MORE GUNS . . . BEAT DRUMS!
NO MORE GUNS . . . BEAT DRUMS!

Let's make the world a safer place,
On ev'ry ocean and land,
It's up to us together,
So let's take a stand,
Sing out loud and clear,
Against hate and fear.
NO MORE GUNS . . . BEAT DRUMS!
NO MORE GUNS . . . BEAT DRUMS!

How can we have a better world,
And live in harmony?
How can we settle our differences,
Peacefully?
Let's put an end to war,

Forevermore.
NO MORE GUNS . . . BEAT DRUMS!
NO MORE GUNS . . . BEAT DRUMS!

Rap improvisation by the students:

Imagine a world without hate,
We are the masters of our fate.
NO MORE GUNS . . . BEAT DRUMS!
NO MORE GUNS . . . BEAT DRUMS!

Don't do drugs,
Let's have lots of hugs.
NO MORE GUNS . . . BEAT DRUMS!
NO MORE GUNS . . . BEAT DRUMS

No more fights,
Let's talk it out
NO MORE GUNS . . . BEAT DRUMS!
NO MORE GUNS . . . BEAT DRUMS!

I know what to say,
Let's have peace today.
NO MORE GUNS . . . BEAT DRUMS!
NO MORE GUNS . . . BEAT DRUMS!

We are here to say that we need peace,
Not tomorrow but today.
NO MORE GUNS . . . BEAT DRUMS!
NO MORE GUNS . . . BEAT DRUMS!

Stop the violence, stop the hate,
Let's get together and celebrate!
NO MORE GUNS . . . BEAT DRUMS!
NO MORE GUNS . . . BEAT DRUMS!

This chant resounded in the auditorium of the Lincoln Academy where the entire student body witnessed a demonstration by the model group. It was inspiring and gave tremendous hope to see the faces of these students and hear them chant over and over, in unison:

No MORE GUNS. . . BEAT DRUMS!

SIXTH MOVEMENT

THE MIRACLE CONTINUES

If the demands of our modern world and the
progressivemultiplications of stress and strain are
to be met with . . . healthy instinct, we must try to
re-establish a continuity . . . based on a substance
which has remained continuous . . . [Humankind's]
ultimate leap is through music. . . .

—Yehudi Menuhin

INTO THE FUTURE: NOTES FROM MY PERSPECTIVE

> We all need to be healed in the highest sense . . .
> mind, body, and spirit. The first step is to realize
> that this is . . . possible.
>
> —Deepak Chopra

> When you do things from your soul,
> you feel a river moving in you, a joy.
>
> —Jalaluddin Rumi

With passage into the twenty-first century, we music therapists have more than ever an imperative to heighten and broaden our vistas—to effect an impact globally that reaches far beyond the traditional treatment room. We must look to new ways and possibilities for bringing the essence of music therapy—its profound humanness—to the "ordinary" people of planet Earth. Our intention is attainable. For *we music therapists have as our therapeutic agent a universal means of human contact, communication, and expression—music*. The potential is unbounded. The miracle goes on. . . .

And so, let us envision fully utilizing our unique methods and skills to address all-pervasive "problems in living." We need to have music therapists in public schools, in nursery schools, in community centers, in religious institutions, in corporate settings, in war-torn zones around the world using music therapy methods and techniques for the wellness of the public-at-large. We need to give special attention to the children—the young people—who are just finding their way in a world that isn't, to say the least, always friendly.

CELEBRATE MUSIC THERAPY

Music therapy is a quintessential modality whose benefits can bring well-being on every level of existence to individuals and groups of all ages, heritages, conditions, and societal strata. Expanding and heightening the humanistic scope of our work, we need to constantly remind ourselves that the very nature of our modality offers means of meeting challenges lovingly and peacefully, of enhancing the quality of life of untold numbers of people; of bridging differences, honoring commonalities, and effecting unity in diversity. In the book, *Planethood: The Key To Your Future* (Ferenz & Keyes, 1991), Pérez de Cuéllar, Secretary-General of the United Nations in 1990 encourages us to ". . . look forward with confidence to the future that is opening before us—a future that, only a short time ago seemed inconceivable" (p.xv). On that promising and uplifting note, I want to point out that music therapists around the world are already fulfilling a humanitarian mission through the conscious use of music.

The universality of music makes going beyond the traditional treatment room a natural extension of our work. And, aligning with the viewpoint, as Deepak Chopra articulates it, that we all need to be healed, the thought has come to me that, metaphorically speaking, *the planet is the treatment room!*

According to Thomas Berry (1992), an octogenarian and one of the most brilliant sociological historians of our time, humankind is suffering from a pathology he categorizes as autism, namely a lack of aware concern—actually disregard—for the health and ecological balance of the human species, animal species, the environment, natural resources, the very source of life. However, he speaks passionately of the possibilities of renewal, and in a personal communication, fully agreed that music therapy has a decisive role to play in this renewal. Utterly inspired by this optimistic stance, I wrote an eighteen-stanza musical invocation to planet Earth with a rhythmic figured-bass vocal accompaniment: "Celebrate Us All Together As a Universe Symphony."

At a Music Therapists for Peace plenary session of The World Federation of Music Therapy Congress in Spain in 1993, this composition was performed in many languages by music therapists selected to represent different countries, with attendees from around the world vocalizing a figured bass on the universal syllable "la" and at the end of each stanza intoning the refrain:

Celebrate us all together,
As a Universe Symphony.

This was a stirring demonstration of how profoundly a large group can be moved by a music therapy-oriented approach to raising awareness and tapping into feelings. Many rushed to me in tears of sadness and joy, as the appeal for celebration and renewal came to a finale on an impassioned note:

> Celebrate the healing power of music,
> Celebrate music therapy,
> Celebrate us all together,
> As a Universe Symphony.

This musical expression was living proof that individuals—human beings whatever their language, whatever their culture, whatever their lifestyle—can experience becoming a unified whole through the *conscious* use of music. It was designed to send out the message to music therapists—and was received and welcomed with heartening enthusiasm—*that we are limited only by our own inspiration and aspiration*; that, as we move into the next millennium, there will be unbounded opportunities and possibilities for bringing health and healing on a global scale. This can come about as our perspective grows individually and collectively; and as our understanding and perception of the nature of our modality continues to deepen and broaden.

Let the planet sing . . . let the miracle of music therapy prevail . . .

CONCLUDING NOTE

Love is the moving principle of
all forms of relationship. Love
transforms. Love purifies.

—Swami Shivanada

Dear reader,

To my family—children and grandchildren, "adopted" Argentineans included—call me "Muvvy." Their love and light shine on me, giving me the courage, the heart, the strength, the passion to go on and on and on. All through the writing of this book, I have given them progress reports—how I'm holding up, what stage the book is in, which draft I'm working on, etc. etc. Over the wires from Boston, from Tampa, from Memphis, from Tallahassee, from Argentina, from New York, I hear, "Muvvy, I can't wait to read your new book." I laughingly answer, "I can't wait either!"

My Tao as a music therapist—as a parent-grandparent-human being has been shaped by love expressed through music. From the moment my daughter Emily and son Paul were in my arms, they were "fed" music morning, noon, and night. All though their growing years songs, songs, songs were an organic ingredient of their daily diet. Is it any wonder that today both Paul, who is on the faculty of Harvard Medical School doing worldwide work that focuses on the connection between health and ecology and Emily, who was a teacher of seven year olds and now works in the field of health with her periodontist husband, are staunch supporters of my work as a music therapist! Emily has arranged presentations of my work in Tampa, Florida and has become the self-appointed agent of my book, *Music Therapy for the Developmentally Disabled* there! Paul and my daughter-in-law Adrienne who live in Boston, were there for me when Music Therapists for Peace was founded in March of 1988 at a national conference of the American Association for Music Therapy in Boston.

Being and doing music with my granddaughter, Jesse, and my three grandsons Steve, Ben, and Jason has highlighted my journey. I was with each one, at or very soon after their births, straddling the East coast—New York to Tampa, New York to Boston—connecting with them musically. Over the years, I would arrive laden with an autoharp or an omnichord, and a variety of drums and Latin percussion. On one visit to Boston, when Paul's daughter Jesse—my first grandchild—was eight she made known, in no uncertain terms, that she just *had to have a piano*. In a hop, skip, and jump, I saw that she not only had her heart's desire but gave her a start on the keyboard. Ben, Paul's son, was singing beautifully at an early age and at fourteen was an absolute fire-brand on the trap drum he had accumulated and the bongos I gave him. Currently, he is "into" music and with a friend has set up a recording studio where they produce original cassettes of a special genre that they have created. Whenever I went to Tampa where my daughter lives or had family get-togethers at my apartment in New York, Steve and Jason, Emily's sons, from infancy on were featured music makers on the many cassette recordings of wonderful musical times together. And when the final draft of my first book was to be submitted, I had been working on it in Tampa. Steve, then twelve, carried a *very heavy* manuscript to the post office for me. When the book was actually published, he could take pride in having helped it on its way! And "Bird of Light" has been a link with Jason. Since he was a year old, I have sung it to and with him. We have had a great time record-ing it together. To this day, it has a very special meaning for us.

To know that my being a parent and a grandparent, being a music therapist, "being peace" are one and the same—a contin-uum for my family—fills my heart. That they associate music and peace and, I do believe, unconditional love with who I am, and if being a music therapist contributes to a better present and future for them and their children and their children and their children, my journey—my Tao will have its deeply intended meaning.

MY LOVE FOREVER,

Edith Hillman Boxill

REFERENCES

Alvin, J. (1978). *Music therapy for the autistic child*. London: Oxford University Press.

Arguelles, J. (1987). *The Mayan factor*. Santa Fe NM.: Bear & Company.

Ashton-Warner, S. (1964). *Teacher*. New York: Bantam Books.

Bentov, I. (1980). "Sound waves and vibrations." In L. Bentov (ed.) *Stalking the wild pendulum: On the mechanics of consciousness*. New York: Bantam Books.

Bolen, J. S. (1982). *The Tao of psychology: Synchronicity and the self*. New York: HarperCollins.

Boxill, E.H. (1974). *Developing communication with the autistic child through music therapy*. ERIC Document Reproduction Service, Ed 149 534 and EC 103 762.

———. (1976). *Music therapy with the developmentally handicapped*. Folkways Cassette Series 0610, The Smithsonian Institution (booklet included).

———. (1981). A continuum of awareness: Music therapy with the developmentally handicapped. *Music Therapy* 1 (1), 17—23.

———.(1985). *Music therapy for the developmentally disabled*. Austin, TX: Pro-Ed, Inc.

———. (1989). *Music therapy for living*. St. Louis, MO: MMB Music Inc.

———. (1996). On cycles: beginnings, endings, beginnings. *Music Therapy* 13 (2)

———. (1997). Multicultural music therapy: A global imperative. *Music Therapy Perspectives* (in press).

Bruscia, K. E. (1987). *Improvisational models of music therapy.* Springfield, IL: Charles C Thomas.

Bruscia, K. E., Hesser, B., and Boxill, E. H. (1981). Essential competencies for the practice of music therapy. *Music Therapy* 1 (1), 45–49.

Calvin, S. H. (1990). *The cerebral symphony: Seashore reflections on the structure of consciousness.* New York: Bantam Books.

Capra, F. (1980). *The Tao of physics.* New York: Bantam Books.

Chen, S. (1991). *The Tao of voice.* Rochester,VT: Destiny Books.

Chopra, D. (1993). *Ageless body, timeless mind.* New York: Harmony Books.

———. (1994). *Journey into healing: Awakening the wisdom within you.* New York: Harmony Books.

Diallo, Y., and Hall, M. (1989). *The healing drum: African wisdom teachings.* Rochester,VT: Destiny Books.

Erikson, E. H. (1963). *Childhood and society.* (2nd edition.) New York: Norton.

Handy, W. C. (ed.) (1949). *A Treasury of the Blues.* New York: Charles Boni Publisher/Simon and Schuster, Inc.

Hanh, T. N. (1987). *The miracle of mindfulness.* Boston: Beacon Press.

———. (1992). *Peace is every step.* New York: Bantam Books.

Hayward, J. (1995). *Sacred world.* New York: Bantam Books.

Heider, J. (1986). *The Tao of leadership: Lao Tzu's Tao Te Ching* (adapted). New York: Bantam Books.

Hillman, J. (1996). *The soul's code: In search of character and calling.* New York: Random House.

Janson, H. W. (1985). *19th-century sculpture.* New York: Harry N. Abrams, Inc.

Jung, C. G. (1959). *The undiscovered self.* New York: The American Library.

Landeck, B. (1950). *Songs to grow on.* New York: Edward B. Marks Music Corporation.

———. (1961). *Echoes of Africa in the folk songs of the Americas.* New York: David McKay Company.

Langer, S. K. (1942). *Philosophy in a new key.* New York: Mentor Books.

Lingerman, H. A. (1983). *The healing energies of music.* Wheaton, IL: The Theosophical Publishing House.

Maslow, A. H. (1976). *The farther reaches of human nature.* New York: Penguin Books.

May, R. (1972). *Power and innocence: A search for the sources of violence.* New York: Delta Books.

Neruda, P. (1986). *Blessed are the peacemakers.* (A 1987 calendar.) Berkeley, CA:Golden Turtle Press.

Nordoff, P.,and Robbins, C. (1971). *Therapy in music for handicapped children.* New York: St. Martin's Press.

———. (1977). *Creative music therapy.* New York: The John Day Company.

Perls. F. S. (1966). Gesalt therapy and human potentialities. In H. A. Otto (ed.) *Exploration in human potentialities.* Springfield, IL: Charles C Thomas.

———. (1974). *Gestalt therapy verbatim.* New York: Bantam Books.

———. (1976). *The Gestalt approach and eyewitness to therapy.* New York: Bantam Books.

Raposo, J., and Moss, J. (1971). *The Sesame Street song book.* New York: Simon and Schuster.

Rogers, C. R. (1971). *On becoming a person.* Boston: Houghton Mifflin.

Rose, S. (1973). *The conscious brain.* New York: Alfred A. Knopf.

Roskam, K. S. (1993). *Feeling the sound: The influence of music on behavior.* San Francisco: San Francisco Press, Inc.

Rudd, E. (ed.) (1984). *Music and healing.* Oslo, Norway: Norsk Musikforlag A/S.

Rutter, M., and Schopler, E. (eds.) (1964). *Autism: A reappraisal of concepts and treatment.* New York: Plenum Press.

Severin, F. T. (1965). *Humanistic viewpoints in psychology.* New York: McGraw Hill.

Stevens, J. O. (1980). *Awareness: Exploring, experimenting, experiencing.* New York: Bantam Books.

Swimme, B.and Berry, T. (1992). *The universe story: A celebration of the unfolding of the cosmos.* San Francisco: Harper San Francisco

Szaaz, T. S. (1974). *The myth of mental illness.* New York: Harper & Row.

Talbot, M. (1992). *The holographic universe.* New York: Harper Perennial.

Tame, D. (1984). *The secret power of music.* Rochester, VT: Destiny Books.

Wakefield, D. (1995). *Expect a miracle.* San Francisco: Harper San Francisco.

Wilhelm, H., and Baynes, C. F. (1968). *The I Ching or Book of changes*. Bollingen Series XIX, Princeton, NJ: Princeton University Press.

Wing, L. (1974). *Autistic children*. Secaucus, NJ: The Citadel Press.

Zinker, J. (1978). *Creative process in Gestalt therapy*. New York: Vintage Books.

Zukav, G. (1979). *The dancing Wu Li Masters*. New York: William Morrow and Company, Inc.

APPENDIX:
SONGS USED IN ANECDOTAL ACCOUNTS

In order of their use:

"Pop! Goes the Weasel"
"See How I'm Jumping"
"La Cucaracha"
"Day by Day"
"Donald's Blues"
"Sing"
"Jimmy Crack Corn"
"Sometimes I Feel Like a Motherless Child"
"Kum Ba Ya"
"Ave Maria"
"Roo Koo Bay"
"I Love Trash"